I am a cloud in the heaven's height,
The stars are lit for my delight,
Tireless and changeful, swift and free,
I cast my shadow on hill and see—
But why do pines on the mountain's crest
Call to me always, "Rest, rest."

I throw my mantle over the moon
And I blind the sun on his throne at noon,
Nothing can tame me, nothing can bind,
I am a child of the heartless wind—
But, oh, the pines on the mountain's crest
Whispering always, "Rest, rest."

—Sara Teasdale

Over the Moon

An anthology
compiled and edited by

Zena Sutherland and **Marilyn F. Cunningham**

Program Authors

Carl Bereiter
Valerie Anderson
Ann Brown
Marlene Scardamalia
Walter Kintsch
Joseph Campione

Open Court
La Salle, Illinois

President and Publisher
M. Blouke Carus

Education Director
Carl Bereiter

Project Coordination
Marsha Roit

Project Planning and Implementation
Thomas G. Anderson
Commonwealth Strategies, Inc.

Senior Editor
Marilyn Cunningham

Permissions
Diane Sikora

Art Direction
Todd Sanders

Cover Design
James Buddenbaum

Acknowledgments

Grateful acknowledgment is given to the following publishers and copyright owners for permission granted to reprint selections from their publications. All possible care has been taken to trace ownership and secure permission for each selection included.

Abingdon Press, for "Trina," adapted from *Trina's Boxcar* by Patricia Miles Martin; copyright © 1967 by Abingdon Press.

Isaac Asimov, for "Benjamin Franklin Changes the World," reprinted from *Cricket* Magazine; copyright © 1976 by Isaac Asimov.

Atheneum Publishers, Inc.: for an adaptation of *Santiago's Silver Mine* by Eleanore Clymer, copyright © 1973 by Eleanore Clymer; and for "Mother, a Dog Is at the Door," from *One Winter Night in August and Other Nonsense Jingles* by X. J. Kennedy (A Margaret K. McElderry Book), copyright © 1975 by X. J. Kennedy.

Atheneum Publishers, Inc., and McIntosh and Otis, Inc., for "Earthquake," from *The Way Things Are and Other Poems* by Myra Cohn Livingston (A Margaret K. McElderry Book); copyright © 1974 by Myra Cohn Livingston.

Mary Buckley, for "How the Farmer's Wife Took Care of Things," illustrated by Robin & Jocelyn Wild, reprinted from *Cricket* Magazine; text © 1976 by Mary Buckley, illustrations © 1976 by Open Court Publishing Company.

Caponi, Terchik, and Bayard, trustees for the estate of Frances M. Frost, for "Night Plane" by Frances M. Frost.

Clarion Books/Ticknor & Fields, a Houghton Mifflin Company, for "Parties and Pastimes in the Old West," from *Children of the Wild West* by Russell Freedman; copyright © 1983 by Russell Freedman.

Contemporary Books, Inc., Chicago, for "The Chippewa" and "Kevin Cloud," from *Kevin Cloud* by Carol Ann Bales; copyright © 1972 by Carol Ann Bales.

Coward, McCann & Geoghegan, Inc., and Curtis Brown, Ltd., for "Contest Fever," from *What's the Prize, Lincoln?* by Dale Fife; copyright © 1971 by Dale Fife.

Thomas Y. Crowell and Curtis Brown, Ltd., for "Memories," excerpted from *Sister* by Eloise Greenfield; copyright © 1974 by Eloise Greenfield. Based on a short story, "Dream Panoply," by Eloise Greenfield, which originally appeared in *Negro Digest*, January 1970.

Thomas Y. Crowell and Harold Ober Associates, for an excerpt from *The Big Wave* by Pearl S. Buck; copyright 1947 by The Curtis Publishing Co., copyright 1948, 1976 by Pearl S. Buck, published by The John Day Company.

Dial Books for Young Readers and Nicholasa Mohr, for "Thanksgiving," adapted from *Felita* by Nicholasa Mohr; text copyright © 1979 by Nicholasa Mohr.

Illustration

Angela Adams (401, 402, 405, 407); Joanna Adamska-Koperska (369, 370, 373); Bill and Judie Anderson (138, 140, 142–144, 230, 408); Ray App (265, 269); George Armstrong (111–113, 115, 116); Sal Asaro (304, 307, 309); Lois Axeman (94, 258); Robert Baumgartner (222–223); Robert Borja (52–55, 124); Irene Brady (131, 133, 135, 136); Nan Brooks (205); Eva Cellini (cover, 200); Joseph Cellini (92–93, 158); Steve Clay (125, 128, 129); Jim Cummins (10–13); David Cunningham (67, 69, 318, 321, 322, 325, 366, 367); Bert Dodson (71–77, 79, 99–102, 104–105, 245, 247, 249–250, 428, 430–431, 433); Pat Doyle (28); Tom Dunnington (284, 286, 289–292); Mike Eagle (97–98, 259, 260, 262, 397–400); Larry Frederick (271, 272); Hal Frenck (211–215, 217, 219–221, 293, 294); Pam Frost (270); Michael Hague (417, 419, 421, 423, 425, 427); George Hamblin (80–81); Linda Heller (201, 202, 204); Dennis Hockerman (82, 106, 107, 109, 226–228, 295, 385); Dora Leder (83–85, 87–90, 173–175, 177, 179, 181, 184, 186); Diana Magnuson (193–195, 198); Dick Martin (2–4, 206, 310); Robert Masheris (394, 395); Charles McBarron (296, 297, 299, 300, 303); Carolyn McHenry (9, 416); Yoshi Miyake (117, 270); Tak Murakami (14–19); Mark Paternostro and JoAnn Daley (130); Diane Paterson (172); Monica Santa (63, 235, 237, 239, 240, 242); Gene Sharp (167–170, 171); Dan Siculan (41, 43–45, 47, 49–50, 386–388, 392); Krystyna Stasiak (231–233); Arvis Stewart (118–120, 122, 123); Jozef Sumichrast (154–157); George Suyeoka (159–161, 165, 166, 357–359, 361–363, 365); George Ulrich (311, 313–317, 344, 345, 347, 349, 350, 353, 355); Dick Wahl (150, 151, 153); Jack Wallen (252, 254, 256); David Wiesner (29–32, 34–36, 38); Jan Wills (6–7)

Photography

Colorado Historical Society (409); Culver Pictures (147, 278, 280, 282, 318); Denver Public Library, Western History Department (412, 414); Historical Society of Pennsylvania (64–65); Idaho State Historical Society (410, 413); Editorial Photocolor Archives (145, 146); Dan Morrill (148, 149); Photo Researchers, Inc. (8)

Contents

Unit One
Monstrous Creatures

Unit Two
Friendship

Unit Three
Beginnings

Unit Four
Flying

Unit Five
Understanding Others

Unit Six
Changes

Unit Seven
Achievements

Unit Eight
Disasters

Unit Nine
Pastimes

Unit One
Monstrous Creatures

Harry and the Whatzit

DICK GACKENBACH

I knew there was something terrible down in the cellar. I just knew, because the cellar was dark and damp and it smelled.

"Don't go down there," I told my mother.

"Why?" she asked.

"There is something terrible down there."

"I have to go down in the cellar," she said. "We need a jar of pickles." She never believes me!

I waited and waited and waited at the cellar door. She never came back up.

Someone had to do something, so I took a broom and went down the cellar steps. It was very black and gloomy. And it smelled.

"I know there is something here," I called out. "What did you do with my mother?"

Then I saw it! A double-headed, three-clawed, six-toed, long-horned Whatzit. It was hiding behind the furnace.

"Where is my mother?" I asked it.

"The last time I saw your mother," the Whatzit said, "she was over by the pickle jars, Runt."

I was sure the Whatzit was lying. "What did you do with her?" I shouted, and I gave it a swat with the broom. WHAM!

That made the Whatzit really mad and it came after me. I swung the broom again. WHAM! The Whatzit didn't like that at all.

It climbed up on the washer and I hit it right where it sits down. I noticed the Whatzit was getting smaller. And when I pulled its tail, it got even smaller.

3

Now the Whatzit was down to my size. "Okay, you
better tell me what you did with my mother," I said. "Or
else!"

"Kid, you're crazy," the Whatzit answered. One of the
heads made a face at me. Just for that I twisted a nose,
and the Whatzit shrank some more.

"Why are you getting so small?" I asked.

"Because you aren't afraid of me anymore," the
Whatzit said. "That always happens just when I'm
beginning to feel at home in a closet or a cellar." The
Whatzit looked very sad.

4

The Whatzit got smaller and smaller and smaller. Just when it was about the size of a peanut, I called out, "Try Sheldon Parker's cellar next door. He's afraid of everything."

"Thanks," I heard it say. Then the Whatzit was gone. It disappeared before it could tell me what it had done to my mother.

I looked in the washer. She was not in there. I looked behind some boxes. My mother was not there either. I looked inside the wood bin. No mother there. I was very worried.

Then I found her glasses beside the pickle jars. But what had happened to the rest of her? I was searching for more clues when I discovered the back cellar door was open.

I looked outside, and there in the bright sunlight was my mother picking flowers. Boy, was I glad to see her.

"I found your glasses in the cellar," I said.

"Thank you, Harry," she said. "But I thought you were afraid of the cellar."

"Not anymore," I answered. "The terrible Whatzit is gone. I chased it away with the broom!"

"Well," she said, "I never saw a Whatzit down there." She never believes me.

I helped her carry the pickles into the kitchen where she gave me some milk and cookies.

"You know what, Harry," my mother said. "I will never worry about a Whatzit as long as you are around." Maybe she did believe me.

Later I heard an awful yell coming from the house next door. I'll bet Sheldon looked in the cellar.

5

The Strangest Mammal
THE DUCKBILL PLATYPUS

HOWARD E. SMITH, JR.

In 1799, Dr. George Shaw, a curator at the British Museum in London, received a package from Australia. When he opened it, he found the skin of a very unusual animal. At first glance, it looked like the skin of a mammal, for it was covered with fur, and only mammals have fur. But the head of the animal had a bill that looked like a duck's bill. That was puzzling. How could a mammal have a bill like a bird's?

Shaw could not believe it. For a while he and other scientists thought the skin might be a hoax. People had played tricks with animals before. They had sewn monkey heads on fish and sold them as mermaids. Had someone sewn a duck's bill onto the skin of an unknown animal?

British scientists examined the skin very carefully and found that nothing was sewn together. It was obviously the skin of a genuine animal, one that was completely new to science. But what sort of animal was it? The scientists couldn't agree about that. Some pointed out that if the animal were a mammal, the mother would produce milk. But how could a young mammal suck milk with a bill? A few scientists thought it might be a reptile. Some prehistoric reptiles, such as the duck-billed dinosaurs, had had bills.

In 1824, a German professor, J. F. Meckelt, went to Australia. He saw a live duck-billed animal for himself and discovered that it laid eggs. He also discovered that the female produced milk in an unusual way. It oozed out of the skin at her belly, and the young lapped it up.

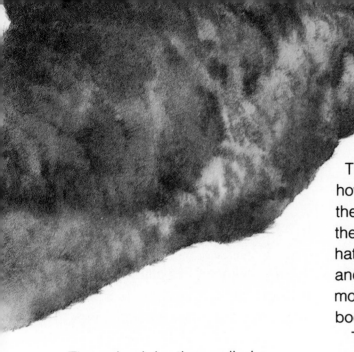

The animal, by then called a duckbill platypus, became the focus of heated debates among scientists. For years they argued about it. Those who chose to call it a reptile pointed out that it laid eggs, had a bill, and had no teeth. Reptiles laid eggs, and a few rare reptiles were known to have bills. Moreover, all birds, which are close relatives of reptiles, have bills and no teeth. Most mammals do have teeth. Many scientists, seeing that the argument could go on forever, suggested placing the animal in a class all by itself. Today, the duckbill platypus is called a mammal, but few are satisfied with that classification.

The reproduction cycle of the duckbill interests scientists the most, for it is unlike that of most other mammals. All but one other give birth to live young. The female duckbill lays eggs, however, as do reptiles. She lays them deep inside a burrow where they will be safe. When the eggs hatch, the female lies on her back, and the young crawl on her. Their motion causes milk to ooze from her body, and the young lap it up.

Today, duckbills are found in streams in southern Australia and in Tasmania. These animals make extremely long burrows—some reaching fifty feet in length—in the banks of rivers and streams. The duckbill builds its burrow so narrow that it can hardly squeeze through. There is an interesting reason for this. The sides of the burrow act as a towel. When a duckbill wiggles through after swimming in the water, its fur is squeezed dry.

The duckbill feeds on small fish, worms, and freshwater clams. It has a huge appetite and eats more than its weight in food each day. Those in zoos must be fed almost all the time. In the wild the duckbill is an excellent hunter. Although it has good sight and hearing, it usually hunts underwater in murky places.

There its bill proves useful. The bill is not hard, as many people think. It becomes hard when the animal dies, but when the animal is alive, the bill is soft and filled with very sensitive nerves. Using its bill, the duckbill feels for things in the murky streams where it feeds.

Duckbills look like cuddly little animals that would make cute pets. Actually, they are very dangerous. The males have spurs on their hind legs that are connected to poison glands. A stab from a spur can make your arm swell up and leave you feeling sick for months.

Duckbill fossils date from almost two million years ago. Because the duckbill platypus seems to be such a primitive mammal, closely related to reptiles, scientists feel sure that much older fossils must exist. The duckbill may even go back to the age of the dinosaurs, which ended sixty million years ago.

No one knows exactly why the duckbill has survived for such a long time, but it has several things in its favor. First of all, it lives in Australia and Tasmania. These two places have been separated from Asia, and from all other large land masses, for at least 100 million years. Animals in Australia and Tasmania were protected from predators such as leopards, wolves, and foxes. No such powerful, quick, and intelligent animals ever hunted the duckbills. Secondly, because the duckbill is such a good swimmer, it could easily escape any predators that might be around on land. It could also retreat into its burrow. Finally, the male's poison spurs would discourage any enemies. All of these factors have probably helped it to survive and to remain one of the most curious animals we know.

Mother, a Dog Is at the Door

Mother, a dog is at the door
Demanding your moleskin hat.
  No, daughter my child, it drives dogs wild,
  We don't dare give him that.

Mother, he said he'd take instead
Your billy goat's old canoe.
  Good gracious, no! That isn't to go,
  It's stuck fast with airplane glue.

Mother, he'd trade some lemonade
For your bicycle-pumpkin pie.
  Oh, would he, the bum? If I lost one crumb
  Of that delicate stuff I'd die!

Mother, I'm scared! He's all bristly-haired!
He's foaming like canned whipped-cream!
  Tell him, my dear, that indeed I fear
  I shall stand on my head and scream.

Oh, Mother, he's peeling his teeth away—
It's Father in dog's disguise!
  Why, daughter my own, I ought to have known
  That a dog wouldn't want my *pies.*

—X. J. Kennedy

Amapola and the Butterfly

PURA BELPRÉ

Along the road between the villages of Las Marias and Maricao in Puerto Rico, the land rises in a great rocky hill. Among the rocks are deep dark caves, mysterious and terrible. Strange tales are told about the caves, stories passed down from the time when the land belonged to the Indians.

Long ago, in that far-off time, there lived in those parts an Indian girl called Amapola. She was very beautiful. She loved the trees of the forest, the flowers in the green meadows, and the animals that shared her world.

When she was a little girl, her mother hung a small idol—a *cemí*—on a string around Amapola's neck. It was supposed to protect her from evil spirits. As she grew up, Amapola was told about strange happenings in the forest beyond her home. She was warned above all about the forest witch who lured people to her cave. Those who followed her were never seen again.

One day, when her mother was in the house and her father in the field, Amapola went to gather some flowers. As she moved about among the flowers, a beautiful butterfly flew out of the forest and fluttered over her head. She stopped to admire its colors, and suddenly she wanted, more than anything else in the world, to hold the butterfly in her hand.

She circled around, stretching out her arms every time the butterfly flew close. Once it flew so near that its wings brushed the tips of her fingers. But no matter how hard she tried to catch it, the butterfly was always out of reach. This made Amapola all the more determined.

11

The butterfly fluttered away and after it went the girl. In and out among the trees it flew, and in and out went Amapola. On and on, higher and higher into the forest they went. Then suddenly the butterfly disappeared, and just as suddenly a frightful-looking, shaggy-haired woman stood before the girl.

"You have lost the butterfly," she said, "but do not grieve. Come, I'll take you to that butterfly and to many others far more beautiful. Come!"

And like one under a spell, Amapola followed her.

Up and up, deeper and deeper into the forest they went. Finally they came to a great cave, and the woman led the way inside. It was dark as midnight. Amapola shut her eyes for a second, and when she opened them, the woman was gone. There were no butterflies. The cave was filled with strange rocks, large and small.

Some were shaped like people, others like animals. Beads and necklaces were scattered on the floor. Curious scribblings and Indian faces were painted on the walls. In the center was a grotesque face. It was the face of the woman who had brought her to the cave.

Suddenly Amapola remembered her mother's warnings. Here was the cave she had spoken of, the cave of the forest witch. The beautiful butterfly and the frightening woman were one and the same!

Amapola shuddered with fear. She turned to go but could not move her feet. They felt heavy as stone. She tried to lift them up, but they seemed rooted to the ground. They had no life, no feeling.

Then her hands brushed against the idol that hung around her neck. She clutched it between her palms and whispered, "Help me! Let your magic power protect me!"

And as she whispered the same words, over and over, a strange prickly feeling crept into her feet and legs. The heaviness was gone. Life was returning. Now she could raise her feet, and she bounded out of the cave and raced down the hillside as fast as she could go. She arrived home still clutching the little stone idol that had saved her.

That night the Indians gathered to hear Amapola's tale. When she had spoken, the elders pondered, wondering whether the rocks in the great cave were the bodies of people and animals that the forest witch had turned to stone. But there was no doubt in Amapola's mind. She was certain that they were. Hadn't she almost become one of them?

Time passed and other people came to live in the land that had belonged to Amapola's tribe. But the Indian tale of Amapola was never forgotten. Mothers still told the story to their children, and to this day no one dares to explore the caves on the rocky hill.

Monster Animals

DANIEL COHEN

The people of the ancient world told stories of a great number of monstrous animals. Most of the stories were just that—stories. No one was really supposed to believe them.

One of these monsters from the myths of the ancient Greeks is the *chimera*. This creature was supposed to have the head and front parts of a lion, the body of a goat, and the hindquarters of a dragon. Sometimes it is shown as a three-headed monster, each part having its own separate head.

To make matters worse, the chimera had a fiery breath. It was able to burn up anything that came near it. The monster was finally killed by the heroic Bellerophon. The hero was riding the winged horse, Pegasus. This allowed him to stay clear of the chimera's fiery breath.

14

The word "chimera" is still a part of our language. It means any wild or unfounded illusion. To say that someone is chasing a chimera means that the person is chasing an impossible dream. That seems to have been the way that the Greeks felt about this monster as well.

But not all of the monster animals of Greek mythology are entirely imaginary. Some were based on facts, though the facts were exaggerated for the purpose of storytelling. One such monster is the *centaur*. This is a creature that was half-man, half-horse. Greek mythology is full of centaur tales. Sometimes the centaurs are good, sometimes evil.

There is no real centaur, and there never was. But the myth is based on something. That something is the mounted nomads that from time to time swept down

15

on Greek-controlled lands. In very early times the Greeks did not ride horses. They used them only to pull carts. The first time the Greeks actually saw people riding horses, they must have been astonished.

The nomads rode very well. It looked as though horse and rider were two parts of the same creature. That is how the legend of the centaur must have begun.

The Greeks were not the only people to have tales of monster animals. From the Middle East come the legends of Sinbad the Sailor. These are full of fantastic beasts. Probably the best known is an enormous bird called the *roc*. The roc was supposed to be so large that it could carry elephants in its talons.

The legend of the roc has many origins. It probably began with exaggerated accounts of eagles. These large, fierce birds have often inspired legends.

Later, Arabian sailors may have brought back giant eggs from their voyages. The eggs, which were nearly the size of a basketball, were not the eggs of a roc. They were the eggs of the elephant bird, an enormous, ostrich-like bird. The elephant bird is now extinct. But a few hundred years ago elephant birds were plentiful on the island of Madagascar. Sailors often carried away elephant-bird eggs as souvenirs. That is one of the reasons the elephant bird is now extinct.

People also reported that they had seen a feather from the roc. What they saw was not a feather at all. It was a leaf from a palm tree that grows on Madagascar. The leaf looks a bit like a giant feather.

It is not hard to imagine that sailors told tall tales of seeing the giant bird. Then they backed up their stories with the giant egg and the giant feather. A lot of people would have believed them.

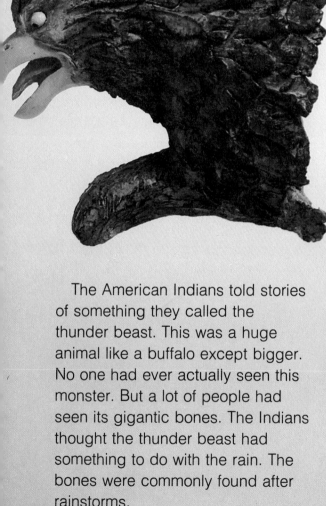

The American Indians told stories of something they called the thunder beast. This was a huge animal like a buffalo except bigger. No one had ever actually seen this monster. But a lot of people had seen its gigantic bones. The Indians thought the thunder beast had something to do with the rain. The bones were commonly found after rainstorms.

In a way these Indian legends were quite correct. The bones did belong to giant animals. But these animals were extinct. They had died out thousands of years before. The bones were buried deep in the earth. Sometimes a strong rain or a flood would wash away the soil and expose the bones on the surface.

The Indians also had tales of a gigantic bird. It was called the thunderbird. These legends may have begun with the eagle, but more likely they were inspired by the California condor. This bird is a giant vulture. It is one of the largest flying birds alive today. It is still very impressive, though it is nowhere near as large as the legendary thunderbird. The California condor is very rare today. Its habitat must be carefully protected to save it from extinction.

The legends of some monster animals are fairly recent. In different parts of England there are legends about the black dog. These stories are only a couple of hundred years old. That is recent as far as legends go.

The black dog is a huge and supernatural hound. It appears on lonely roads and is bad luck to anyone who sees it. Some legends even say it will attack solitary travelers. Sir Arthur Conan Doyle used the legend in one of his most famous Sherlock Holmes stories, *The Hound of the Baskervilles*.

Most of the monster animals that we think of today are even more recent. They are entirely fictional. They were created in the imaginations of movie makers and science fiction writers.

The most popular monster animal from the movies is King Kong. The film *King Kong* was first released in 1933. It was an immediate success. It ranks as one of the three or four best monster movies of all times.

The final scene of *King Kong* is one of the most celebrated in movie history. The giant gorilla, carrying actress Fay Wray in one hand, climbs to the top of the Empire State Building. There he is shot down by airplanes—but not before he manages to swat some of the planes out of the sky.

The idea of the gorilla as a monster did not originate with King Kong. It goes back a long way. When Europeans first began hearing tales of gorillas, they did not know what to think. They could not decide whether the creature was ape or man. They thought it might be some sort of wild man. Many of the stories told of how fierce the creature was.

When Europeans first encountered living gorillas they were terrified. The huge apes roared and beat their chests. The gorilla got the reputation of being the most ferocious beast in the jungle. This reputation was still around when the movie *King Kong* was made.

Today we know that all the stories about ferocious gorillas are just nonsense. The gorilla is very strong. It can be dangerous if it is frightened or annoyed. But ordinarily the gorilla is a very gentle and lazy creature. It likes nothing better than to sit in the shade, eat, and sleep eighteen hours a day.

As long as monster movies are popular, new monsters will have to be invented. In films people seem to want bigger and better (or worse) monsters. At times the movie makers have had to strain to keep up with the demand for more horrors. But the human imagination is equal to the job. We will never run out of monsters.

How the Farmer's Wife Took Care of Things

A Folk Tale from Iceland

Translated and Adapted by

Mary Buckley

On a lonely farm in the mountains lived a farmer and his wife. They were neither rich nor poor, and the pride of the farmer's life was his herd of black and white cows.

One day in the late summer, the farmer decided to go down the mountain to the Fair. As he was leaving, he said to his wife, "I may be very late, and you will be all alone. Can you take care of things by yourself?"

"Certainly," said his wife. So the farmer went on his way, and the wife went about her business. She did not mind being alone. She was busy all day, and, as night drew on, she built the fire and took up her sewing. Suddenly, she was startled to see a man standing in the doorway. He was stout, had straw-colored hair, and—although he did not think she saw it—he had a club under his jacket.

"Good evening," said the farmer's wife.

"Where is your husband?" asked the stranger.

"Busy in the barn, but he will be back shortly."

"I will wait," said the stranger and sat down on a stool by the fire.

"Very well," said the wife calmly and went on with her sewing.

"Your husband thinks he is a great man hereabouts?" asked the stranger, in a voice that showed he thought otherwise.

"Great enough," said the wife. "Are you planning to be a great man, too?"

"I could be, if I chose," said he.

"Indeed?" said the wife, in a voice that showed she thought otherwise of *that*.

"Indeed," said the stranger, and he suddenly grew until he was thirteen feet, seven inches tall, and his straw-colored hair brushed the roof beam.

21

If the wife was surprised, she didn't show it. She smiled and said, "Good trick. And yet," she went on thoughtfully, "growing big is easy. Even flowers can grow. But shrinking is another matter. Quite uncommon. I don't suppose you can shrink?"

"Can I shrink?" said the stranger scornfully. "How about this?" And he dwindled to the size of a squirrel. The wife chuckled and picked him up and held him at arm's length.

"Not a bad trick," she agreed. "It would be even better if you could make yourself small enough to fit in my thimble, but I suppose this is the best you can do."

"We'll see about that," said the little man scornfully, and he shrank to the size of a bumblebee. When the farmer's wife saw that, she popped her thimble over him.

"Let me out!" he squeaked.

"I don't think I'd better do that," said she. "I think I'll wait until my husband comes home and see what he says." So she sat with her thumb held firmly over the thimble's opening and waited. Presently, home came the farmer, feeling very jolly.

"Did you have a good time at the Fair?" asked his wife.

"Yes," said he, "and I brought you some ribbons."

"Thank you," said she, "and I have a present for you."

"What is it?"

"Guess what I have in my thimble."

"Your thumb?"

"No," said she. "I have a little man in there. If I hold the thimble up to your ear, you can hear him."

Sure enough, the farmer could hear the stranger swearing fiercely in a tiny voice.

"How did he get in there?" asked the farmer.

His wife told him all about the stranger's arrival and about his hidden club. The farmer thought that his wife had been very clever, but he could not for the life of him think what to do with a little man in a thimble.

At last he tapped politely on the thimble and said, "Sir, are you quite happy in there?"

"No," said the stranger.

"I thought not," said the farmer. "Shall we make a bargain?"

"What sort of bargain?" asked the stranger sulkily.

"If I let you out, will you promise to go away and never come near our farm again?"

"No," said the stranger. "As soon as I get out of here, I am going to grow eighteen feet tall, and then we shall see who makes bargains."

"Oh," said the farmer, and he began idly to shake the thimble between his thumb and forefinger, while he pondered what to do next.

Presently the stranger spoke again, sounding very seasick. "Farmer, I have changed my mind. Let me out, and I promise to go away and never come near your farm again."

"And do you promise not to grow until you are far away from here?"

"Yes," said the stranger.

"Good," said the farmer. Then he took the thimble out to the meadow and turned the stranger loose.

Next morning the farmer and his wife went out to milk their cows, but the animals were nowhere to be seen. The farmer's wife had an idea and hurried out to the meadow. There, under a blackberry bush, she found the whole herd of black and white cows grazing peacefully. The largest of them was only three inches high, and the smallest calf was no bigger than her thumbnail. She gathered the whole herd into her apron and went back to the house.

"I have found the cows," she said, and set the herd on the kitchen table before her startled husband.

"Dear me," said the farmer. "My precious cows! What shall I do with a herd of three-inch cows? That stranger certainly got the best of us!"

The farmer's wife thought for a minute. Then she smiled and whispered something in her husband's ear.

That very day, the farmer went back down the mountain to display his rare collection of three-inch cows at the Fair. From near and far, people came to see the remarkable miniature cattle—especially the tiny calf—and the farmer and his wife became very rich.

What became of the stranger, I never heard.

Monster Riddles

JANE SARNOFF AND REYNOLD RUFFINS

What is a monster's favorite dinner?
Spook-ghetti, ghost beef, and devil's food cake.

Who won the monster beauty contest?
Nobody.

What do ghosts eat for breakfast?
Ghost Toasties and evaporated milk.

What do mummies eat for breakfast?
Shrouded Wheat.

What do ghosts eat for lunch?
Boo-loney sandwiches.

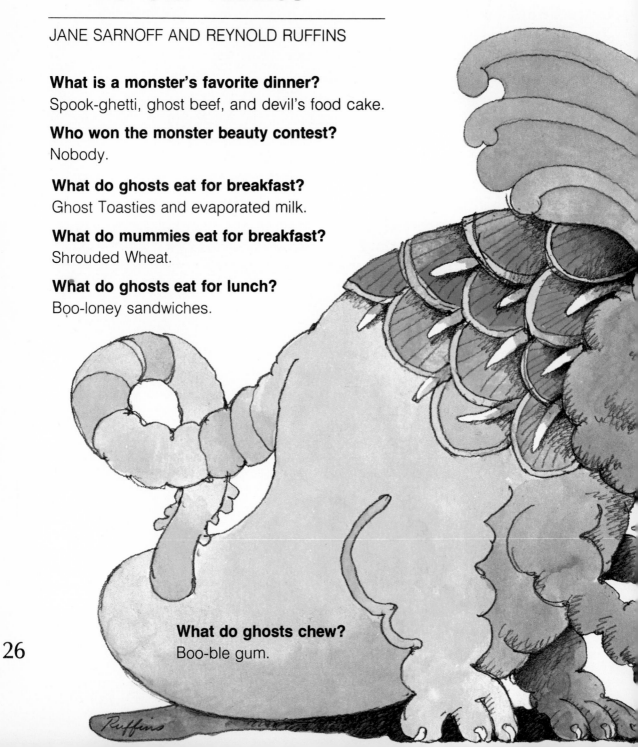

What do ghosts chew?
Boo-ble gum.

How many people can a ghoul eat on an empty stomach?
One. After that its stomach would not be empty.

What sort of beans does a werewolf like?
Human beans.

What could a monster eat after it had its teeth pulled?
Its dentist.

What do you call a clean, neat, hardworking, kind, intelligent, and friendly monster?
A failure.

27

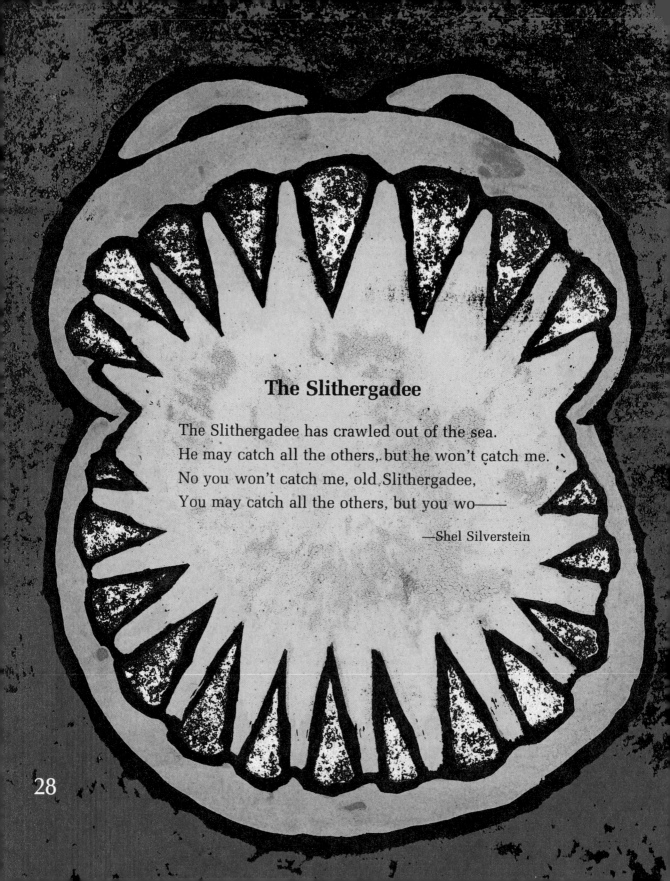

The Slithergadee

The Slithergadee has crawled out of the sea.
He may catch all the others, but he won't catch me.
No you won't catch me, old Slithergadee,
You may catch all the others, but you wo——

—Shel Silverstein

28

Dragon Stew

TOM McGOWEN

Once upon a time there was a kingdom ruled by a king who was so fat that his people called him King Chubby. He was so fond of food that he couldn't bear to be without it for very long.

Eating was his hobby. He began with a big breakfast at eight o'clock. He had a slight snack at ten and a large lunch at twelve. Then he exercised by watching two tennis players, and since exercise gave him an appetite, he ate a small snack at about two in the afternoon.

At four, he had sandwiches and at seven in the evening he happily sat down to a royal banquet. There was one of these every evening, even if the king was the only one at the table.

Eating was so important to him that it affected everything he did. When he fell in love with a duchess from another kingdom, he told her that he would almost rather look at her than eat a whole roast pig. Needless to say, the duchess never spoke to him again.

His love of eating also got him in trouble in other ways. He was always losing his royal cooks. He just couldn't keep from telling them how to improve their cooking. He insisted on making changes in every dish. Since royal cooks are very proud and temperamental, they resented this. Six cooks had already left in a huff.

One evening when the king entered the banquet hall and saw a sandwich on his plate, he knew what had happened.

"Oh, my," he sighed, "I see number seven has left!"

"Yes, your Majesty," replied the majordomo, "he said he could no longer cook for a king who kept changing all his recipes. And now there are no more royal cooks available! None of those you've had will ever come back, and all the others are cooking for other kings. I don't know how to find another cook. There just aren't any!"

The king looked worried for a moment, then brightened. "I know! A royal cook *is* a royal cook because he has the imagination to make up unusual recipes. There must be

30

many good cooks with imagination in my kingdom. We'll have a contest, and the one who tells me the most unusual recipe can be the royal cook!"

The next day proclamations were posted throughout the kingdom inviting all cooks to enter the contest. There was great excitement. All those who considered themselves good cooks, and every cook from every inn in the kingdom, came clamoring to the castle.

They formed a line which began at the back of the castle and wound around to the front. It crossed the drawbridge, entered the gate, jammed the courtyard, and went up the stairs. It flowed into the throne room, where the king was interviewing them. In they came, bowing, smiling hopefully, and offering enough recipes to fill seven fat cookbooks or seventy fat kings.

But to each, King Chubby shook his head. "That's not unusual," he'd say, or "I've had that before."

While this was going on, a shabby young man came trudging up the road toward the castle. He had patched knees and elbows, and the feather in his worn hat was bedraggled. But he had a merry grin, and he was whistling a gay tune. When he saw the long line of people, he asked a soldier, "What's going on?"

"The king's looking for a new royal cook," the soldier replied. "The cook with the most unusual recipe will get the job and will live in the palace off the best of the land!"

"Wouldn't that be wonderful!"

"Well, I don't know," said the soldier. "Cooks don't get along with the king. He tells 'em what to do, puts things in their pots—he all but does the cooking himself."

"You don't say?" said the young man, and he got into line.

"Oh, are you a cook?" asked the soldier.

"I'm just the sort of cook the king wants," he answered, "and I have the most unusual recipe he's ever heard of!"

It was late afternoon when he reached the throne room. The king was looking very glum. Not one cook had offered a recipe he considered unusual. And now the last of them was this ragged fellow who looked far too thin to be much of a cook. "Well, what's your name and recipe?" he asked.

"I'm Klaus Dinkelspiel, your Majesty. My recipe is so unusual, so rare, that I'll wager you've never heard of it. It's—dragon stew!"

The king gasped. "That sounds different. What's in it—besides dragon, of course?"

"Oh, I can't tell you!" exclaimed Klaus. "It has been a secret in my family for thirteen generations."

33

"I understand," nodded the king, "but if we can ever locate a dragon, you must make it for me. However, you can begin preparing an ordinary royal banquet. You are the new royal cook."

Klaus bowed deeply. "And what would you like for dinner?" he asked.

"How about roast pig with applesauce?"

"And would your Majesty care to show me exactly how you want it cooked?" Klaus asked innocently.

The king stared. "You mean you won't care if I offer advice and suggestions? Why, you and I are going to get along just fine!"

So off they went to the kitchen and collected everything the king needed. Then Klaus said, "Now, how would you prepare this, your Majesty?"

King Chubby, greatly delighted, stuffed the pig, trussed it up, and then peeled and sliced the apples.

"How would you cook this, your Majesty?"

34

So the king happily popped the pig into the oven. He alternated between stirring the applesauce and basting and turning the pig.

Klaus watched and kept saying, "Just how I'd have done it. I use the same method."

When the pig was brown and savory and the sauce bubbling merrily, he said, "I thank you for all your suggestions, sire. If you will go to the banquet hall, I'll serve you the banquet I have prepared."

When the king had gobbled up the last piece of pork and soppet of sauce, he announced that it was the finest banquet he'd ever eaten and Klaus was the finest cook he'd ever had. And from then on, the king and his new cook were well satisfied—King Chubby because he now had all his favorite dishes cooked exactly as he liked them, and Klaus because he was living off the best of the land.

One morning a good many months after Klaus had become the royal cook, he was called to the throne room.

When he entered he was horrified to see the Captain of the guard and a dozen scratched and smoke-blackened soldiers surrounding a large cage inside of which was a small, fat dragon.

"Surprise!" beamed the king. "I sent them out to find a dragon months ago, and it's taken all this time to find one. Now you can cook your special dragon stew tonight. I promise I won't try to find out your secret—I won't even set foot in the kitchen today!"

The soldiers carried the cage to the kitchen, set it down, and trooped out. The captain said, "Careful of it, Cook—it bites, scratches, and can shoot fire six inches out of its nose."

Klaus stared at the small dragon. A tear trickled down its cheek. "Are you trying to think of the best way to kill me?" it asked, accusingly. "It isn't fair! I was minding my own business, bothering no one, and suddenly your soldiers attacked me and carried me here to be made into—into stew." It sniffled.

"Believe me, dragon," said Klaus, "I don't want to make you into stew. I didn't think there were any dragons when I made up that silly recipe. I just wanted to fool the king into thinking I was a cook. I couldn't make any stew if my life depended on it—and it probably does. The king will have me beheaded when he finds out that I fooled him."

"Oh, making stew is easy," said the dragon. "You soak the meat in wine and spices, brown it in butter, and simmer it slowly in broth with onions and carrots. I always throw in a few mushrooms and some parsley, too. And then—"

"You can cook?" interrupted Klaus. "I thought dragons only ate raw princesses and things like that."

"Heavens, no!" the dragon shuddered. "Actually, I'm a good cook. Living alone, I've had to do all my own cooking. I've become quite a chef, if I do say so myself." It blew a smoke ring from its left nostril.

Suddenly, Klaus began to grin and nod his head as though he had thought of something.

At seven o'clock, the king hurried into the banquet hall, tingling to taste Klaus's wonderful dragon stew. He watched eagerly as Klaus carried in a steaming bowl and ladled chunks of beautifully browned meat and vegetables swimming in rich gravy onto the king's plate. King Chubby began to gobble. After four helpings, he leaned back with a sigh.

"That certainly is one of the best stews I've ever eaten. What a shame we can never have it again. That was probably the world's last dragon."

"Oh, we can have it as often as you like, your Majesty," Klaus calmly announced. "You see, the thing that makes dragon stew such a rare recipe is that it can only be cooked *by* a dragon! Allow me to present my assistant."

37

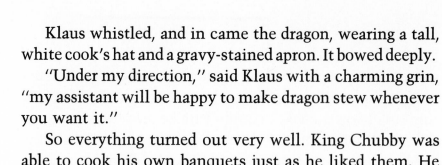

Klaus whistled, and in came the dragon, wearing a tall, white cook's hat and a gravy-stained apron. It bowed deeply.

"Under my direction," said Klaus with a charming grin, "my assistant will be happy to make dragon stew whenever you want it."

So everything turned out very well. King Chubby was able to cook his own banquets just as he liked them. He could also have dragon stew (made from beef) as often as he wanted it. Klaus was happy to be living off the best of the land without having to work hard for it. The dragon was delighted to be an assistant royal cook.

But the happiest of all was the kitchen helper. One of his jobs had been to light the fire in the big stove, and he had always scorched his knuckles. But now he no longer had this task, for the assistant cook lit its own stove by shooting fire out of its nose!

38

Unit Two
Friendship

Polly's Tiger

JOAN PHIPSON

The day before Polly and her parents moved to their new house in the Australian Scrub country, she and her mother went to the zoo.

They had a lovely afternoon. The seals barked. Monkeys jibbered, and a lioness looked at them with big amber eyes and roared. But Polly knew that her favorite animal of them all was the tiger. He did not make a sound. He was not cuddly like the baby bears, and he did not look a bit kind.

He walked silently up and down on the sandy floor in front of his cave, and his coat shone tawny gold in the sun. He was hard and proud and beautiful. He did not even notice the people looking at him. His head was lifted, and he was looking out over the people into the distance. He was a lovely, glittering patch of marmalade on the sandstone rock.

"He is thinking of his subjects in the jungle, I expect," said Polly.

"He hasn't got any friends," said Mrs. Thomas. "But look at him. He doesn't mind."

Two days later Polly stood on the veranda of her new house. It was a lovely day.

"I'll take you to school this morning," said her father. "And after today you can go by yourself. All the children walk to school here. It isn't very far."

40

It was a little early for school when they set off, for Mr. Thomas had to get to work. So the school was empty, except for one of the teachers, when Polly arrived. She showed Polly her classroom and told her to go out into the playground because the other children would be arriving.

Polly sat on a bench and watched them as they passed. They were all chattering and laughing as they came in. But as they walked past her they stopped talking and looked at her instead.

In class it was all right. The teacher was kind and introduced her to the other children.

At lunchtime Polly took her sandwiches and sat fairly near—but not too near—a small group of girls under a tree. Nobody spoke to her at first, but then one of the girls said, "Why have you got a jumper on?"

Polly was the only girl in a jumper. All the others wore pants of various colors. "I don't know," she said. "I thought—I mean, I always wear my jumper at school."

The other girl inspected her from top to toe and then said, "Nobody wears jumpers here." And she turned back to her friends. They all began talking very softly and giggling. Polly guessed they were talking about her, and she felt her face getting red. She put the rest of her sandwiches back in her book bag and pretended she was going to wash her hands.

It was all right again in the afternoon. The teacher asked her two questions she was able to answer. It made her feel better, and when the last class ended she went out feeling quite cheerful.

All the other children were pouring out of the gate into the road. She walked along with them, hoping

someone would say something to her. But nobody did, although several of them turned their heads to look at her. The group grew smaller the farther they went from the school. In the end there were only seven of them.

All of a sudden, to Polly's surprise all the children turned on to a little path that led in among the trees. She did not know where they were going, and nobody told her. Polly walked on alone. It was a long way home.

"Well?" said her mother. "What was it like?"

"It was horrid," Polly said, and burst into tears. "They won't talk to me and they think my jumper's silly, and do I have to go there anymore?"

It took quite a lot of talking and a piece of chocolate cake to make Polly feel there could be a ray of hope in her life. But Mrs. Thomas promised she need not wear her jumper again and told her she must give the other children time to get used to her.

43

As she crawled into bed that night she said, "I don't think I'll be able to sleep. I'm too sad."

"Never mind," said Mrs. Thomas. "Just lie there and think of the loveliest thing you can remember."

So Polly lay in the darkness, trying to think of something lovely. After a time she remembered the tiger, shining like marmalade, walking proudly with his tail flowing out behind, ignoring the people who gaped at him. He was alone and he did not care. In her mind he turned his head and looked at her. He slowly walked toward her. She saw his yellow eyes, his wiry whiskers, and his soft, furry ears. She stood quite still while his tongue came out between the big white teeth and licked her hand. It felt like the roughest sandpaper. She looked him straight in his yellow eyes, proudly, with her chin high. Then she put her hand on the top of his head. He purred with the sound of a vacuum cleaner. Together they walked away from the gaping crowd—the great, sinewy tiger and the girl.

She woke next morning feeling happy. She did not know why she felt happy in spite of school. Then she remembered her tiger, and the thought of him comforted her and made her feel strong. He would walk to school beside her, and neither of them would care what other children thought.

The other children did not know she had come to school with a tiger. They only saw her looking quite ordinary, in pants, and with a friendly smile. They did not see the tiger standing beside her. She thought how astonished they would be if they knew that her hand was on his head. When the bell rang, they all went into the classroom, and the tiger curled himself up comfortably at her feet beneath the desk.

At lunchtime Polly and the tiger sat by themselves under a little tree not far from the big one where most of the other girls and some of the boys were sitting. She was beginning to share her sandwiches with him when one of the bigger girls walked over to her and asked if she would like to sit under their tree. For a moment she wondered if the tiger would mind, but she saw that he had dropped his head on his paws and was sleeping.

"Thank you," she said. "I should like to."

Going home, Polly and her tiger walked together, and a fair-haired girl, whose name was Wendy, and the red-haired boy, whose name was Ted, walked beside them. When they came to the patch of trees where the others had turned off the day before, Wendy said to Polly, "Coming this way? It's shorter."

So she followed the others into the trees, along the narrow, leaf-strewn path, and the tiger padded along behind. A high fence ran along near the path on the right-hand side. Ted and two other boys stopped and went to look through the fence. The small group of girls stopped on the path. Polly waited a little way behind them. The tiger sat at her feet, and she put her hand on his head.

"Can you see him?" said a girl called Sheila.

"He's coming this way," said a boy called Jim.

"He'll have smelled us," said the third boy.

"There he is," said Ted. "Look. He's as big as a calf."

There came a sudden cry from one of the boys, and then Polly saw what it was. A huge black dog loped through the trees, baying as he came. His ears were pricked, and his head was up. Out of his mouth a red tongue lolled. All the boys took a step back from the fence.

"He'll never jump that fence," said Jim. "That's why they put it up. Reckon they don't want to have a murder on their hands on account of the dog."

The dog was quite near the fence now, looking at them and barking. His smooth black coat was shining, and a few flecks of saliva dribbled from his tongue.

Polly remembered the tiger and, with the comfortable feeling that he was walking beside her, turned to go. Just before she reached a bend in the path, she heard a distant whistle. She looked around and saw the great dog turn and bound off among the trees and out of sight.

The next morning Polly walked to school by the road and did not meet any other children until another road joined hers. The tiger had been beside her, but when they all met, he dropped behind.

47

All that morning the sky got darker. By lunchtime the clouds seemed to be lying just above the treetops. When everyone had sat down and pulled out sandwiches, the first big drops fell.

"Come in to the assembly hall. Quickly!" the teacher called. "There's going to be a storm."

All through lunch lightning flashed at the windows and thunder rumbled overhead. But the loudest noise of all was the sound of gallons of water falling on the metal roof of the school.

By the second period the storm began to ease. But now the wind came, rattling the windows. The surrounding trees bowed and swayed in the gusts. At the height of one of the strongest gusts there came a great crash from somewhere not far off.

"That sounded like a tree falling," said the teacher.

When school was out, they all poured out of the open doors onto the sploshy playground. It was a wild afternoon. When they got out of the gate, they saw the river, brown and roaring. And they saw the trees lashing their tops.

Polly went toward the path in the trees and found herself again with all the others from her street. At the corner they all stopped dead. Ted gave a great whistle. "Wow, look at that!"

They all walked in silence toward a huge tree that had fallen across the path. It had been growing on the far side of the fence. The fence had gone over with it and was lying flat on the ground under the tree.

"That was the big crash we heard," said Ted.

"We'll have to climb over it," said Wendy. "There's no way around."

Just beyond the fallen tree the path turned another corner. They went around together—and stopped dead for the second time. Polly heard Jim give a hissing sound, and Beverly yelped.

There, right in front of them, was the big black dog. He was wandering about the path, sniffing. He did not seem to have seen them.

A stick cracked under Jim's foot. The dog looked up. He saw them, threw up his head, and turned to face them. His eyes were wide and brown. His short black ears were pricked. He stood as high as Polly, higher than Wendy, and almost as high as Jim. The children froze.

There was a long silence. Nobody moved.

Polly remembered the tiger beside her. She was sure he was making rumbling noises in his throat. He lifted his head and looked into her face. His tail was twitching a tiny bit. She knew that he had looked once, disdainfully, at the dog, and now he was looking at her again. He got up and took a step forward and waited. At the end of the long, sinewy back, the tail was still twitching. She took a step forward and put her hand on his head. Suddenly she heard her own voice say, "I'm going to walk past that dog."

There was not a murmur from the other children. The tiger started forward and, her hand between his ears, she stepped forward with him. The tiger was between her and the dog. Together they walked on, and the dog turned his head to watch them. They drew level with him, and his nose was level with Polly's chin. She felt his warm breath on her hand. And she was past him. She heard a gasp from the children. Clutching the tiger's coat firmly, she looked around. The dog had got up and was walking after her. His tail waved very faintly. As she walked, he came up on her other side, so that she was between the dog and the tiger. Hardly knowing what she did, she put out her other hand and rested it on the dog's head.

So they came, the three of them, to the end of the path and to the open road. And on the road, walking

down the hill toward her, were two very old ladies. One of them put a small, shining object to her mouth, and Polly heard again the whistle she had heard the previous day.

Immediately, the dog left her side and bounded over to the two ladies. His tail was wagging very amiably now.

"Little girl, what were you doing with Pluto?" demanded the lady with the whistle.

"He was standing in the path, Ma'am. He just—came out with me. Ma'am, there's a tree over your fence. He must have got out."

"In that case we must thank you for bringing him to us. We should not like him to stray."

"Come along, Lucy. Come, Pluto." She strode down the path, the tails of her coat flapping behind her. The other woman and Pluto walked after her.

Strangely, no one had anything to say, and one by one they went in to their own front gates.

The next morning Polly and the others had fun telling everybody else about their adventures with the dog before they went in to school. Ted did most of the telling, and Polly was surprised to hear how brave she had been. That day at lunchtime the tiger was not quite as solid as he had been.

It was a week later that the tiger left her forever. Polly had started down the path with him after school, and all the others had run to catch up. The tiger stopped at the beginning of the path, and she went on without him. He became quite thin and transparent and went quietly out of her mind. She was so busy talking to Ted and Wendy that she did not even see him go. He never came back.

51

About Dolphins

MARGARET DAVIDSON

Dolphins look like fish, and they live where fish live. But they are not fish. They are mammals.

That's why a dolphin comes to the top of the water so often—to breathe air. Fish can breathe in water, but mammals can't. A dolphin breathes air through a tiny hole on top of its head called a blowhole.

Usually a dolphin rises out of the water every half minute or so to open its blowhole and take a gulp of air. But if it has to, a dolphin can hold its breath for six or seven minutes.

A dolphin's ears are two pinholes on the sides of its head. With them, a dolphin can hear all sorts of faint noises in the water—pebbles rolling, sea grasses rustling, and the sounds made by fish and other dolphins.

A dolphin has almost one hundred teeth in its large mouth. These teeth are all the same shape and size. Dolphin teeth are used for catching food, but not for chewing it. A dolphin grabs a fish firmly between the two rows of teeth and swallows it whole.

Dolphins can live out of water for some time if they have to, since they breathe air. But a dolphin must not dry out or it will become overheated. And dolphins do sunburn very easily. So a dolphin out of water must be kept wet at all times.

Most dolphins are very friendly animals. They usually live in a group called a school. Dolphins eat and sleep together in the school. And they help each other in all sorts of ways.

Dolphins have enemies in the sea such as the killer whale and the shark. If a killer whale or a shark comes close, the dolphins make a circle with mothers and babies in the middle. The bigger male dolphins swim around the outside. Usually a shark or a killer whale won't try to attack dolphins in such a group. But if one does, the dolphins fight back together.

Sometimes a dolphin is hurt or sick and needs help. A sick dolphin has a special problem. When people are sick, they can sleep for as long as they want. But if a dolphin sleeps for more than six or seven minutes without coming up for air, it will drown. That is why another dolphin will become the sick dolphin's nurse and swim with it. If the sick dolphin falls too deeply asleep, the nurse will nudge it up for a quick breath of air.

For thousands of years people have felt that there is a special closeness between dolphins and human beings. They have called dolphins our cousins in the sea. There are many stories of wild dolphins following ships. There are stories of dolphins helping people fish. There are even stories of dolphins saving people from drowning by pushing them ashore. And there are wonderful stories of friendships between dolphins and people, especially children.

Dolphins are friendly and fun. They are also useful. Today all sorts of people are studying dolphins—doctors, architects, engineers, and scientists of all sorts. They are finding out many fascinating things.

Dolphins are said to be the fastest swimmers in the sea. So engineers and architects study the dolphin's skin and shape to find ways to make boats go faster through the water.

Dolphins have a special ability to find—and avoid—things in the water, no matter how dark or muddy it is. This natural ability is called sonar. Doctors are interested in dolphin sonar. They hope to make a

kind of sonar that will help blind people move easily in their dark world. Navy scientists are very interested in the dolphin's sonar, too. They hope to improve the mechanical sonar that guides submarines.

Dolphins make all sorts of sounds. They whistle, squeak, squawk, mew, and bark. Some scientists believe these sounds are a real dolphin language. Many scientists are studying these different sounds and trying to understand their meanings.

And many people are studying the dolphin's brain. It is plain that dolphins are very intelligent. Some scientists say they are smarter than dogs. Other scientists say they are even smarter than chimpanzees. This means that dolphins may be smarter than all the animals on earth except people.

Scientists don't always agree about dolphins. But all scientists—and anyone else who knows dolphins—agree about one thing. Dolphins have very definite personalities. Some are shy. Some are show-offs. Some are bright. Some are a little slow to learn. Some are very friendly. Some like to be left alone. There are many different dolphins. And there are many different stories to tell—all of them true.

Blue Moose

MANUS PINKWATER

Mr. Breton had a little restaurant on the edge of the big woods. When winter came, the north wind blew through the trees and froze everything solid. Then it snowed. Mr. Breton didn't like that.

Mr. Breton was a very good cook. Every day people from the town came to his restaurant. They ate gallons of his special clam chowder. They ate plates of his special beef stew. They ate fish stew and special homemade bread. The people from the town never talked much, and they never said anything about Mr. Breton's cooking.

"Did you like your clam chowder?" Mr. Breton would ask.

"Yup," the people from the town would say.

Mr. Breton wished they would say, "Delicious!" or "Good chowder, Breton!" All they ever said was, "Yup." In winter they came on skis and snowshoes.

Every morning Mr. Breton went out behind his house to get firewood. He wore three sweaters, a scarf, galoshes, a woolen hat, a big checkered coat, and mittens. He still felt cold. Sometimes raccoons and rabbits came out of the woods to watch Mr. Breton. The cold didn't bother them. It bothered Mr. Breton even more when they watched him.

One morning there was a moose in Mr. Breton's yard. It was a blue moose. When Mr. Breton went out his back door, the moose was there, looking at him. After a while Mr. Breton went back in and made a pot of coffee while he waited for the moose to go away. It didn't go away. It just

56

stood in Mr. Breton's yard, looking at his back door. Mr. Breton drank a cup of coffee. The moose stood in the yard. Mr. Breton opened the door again. "Shoo! Go away!" he said to the moose.

"Do you mind if I come in and get warm?" said the moose. "I'm just about frozen." He brushed past Mr. Breton and walked into the kitchen. His antlers almost touched the ceiling.

The moose sat down on the floor next to Mr. Breton's stove. He closed his eyes and sat leaning toward the stove for a long time. Wisps of steam began to rise from his blue fur. After a long time the moose sighed. It sounded like a foghorn.

"Can I get you a cup of coffee?" Mr. Breton asked the moose. "Or some clam chowder?"

"Clam chowder," said the moose.

Mr. Breton filled a bowl with creamy clam chowder and set it on the floor. The moose dipped his big nose into the bowl and snuffled up the chowder. He made a sort of slurping, whistling noise.

"Sir," the moose said, "this is wonderful clam chowder."

Mr. Breton blushed a very deep red. "Do you really mean that?"

"Sir," the moose said, "I have eaten some very good chowder in my time, but yours is the very best."

"Oh my," said Mr. Breton, blushing even redder. "Oh my. Would you like some more?"

"Yes, with crackers," said the moose.

The moose ate seventeen bowls of chowder with crackers. Then he had twelve pieces of hot gingerbread and forty-eight cups of coffee. While the moose slurped and whistled, Mr. Breton sat in a chair. Every now and then he said to himself, "Oh my. The best he's ever eaten. Oh my."

Later, when some people from the town came to Mr. Breton's restaurant, the moose met them at the door. "How many in your party, please?" the moose asked. "I have a table for you. Please follow me."

The people from the town were surprised to see the moose. They felt like running away, but they were too surprised. The moose led them to a table, brought them

58

menus, looked at each person, snorted, and clumped into the kitchen. "There are some people outside. I'll take care of them," he told Mr. Breton.

The people were whispering to one another about the moose when he clumped back to the table. "Are you ready to order?" he asked.

"Yup," said the people from the town. They waited for the moose to ask them if they would like some chowder, the way Mr. Breton always did. But the moose just stared at them as though they were very foolish. The people felt uncomfortable. "We'll have the clam chowder."

"*Chaudière de clam*. Very good," the moose said. "Do you desire crackers or homemade bread?"

"We will have crackers," said the people from the town.

"I suggest you have the bread. It is hot," said the moose.

"We will have bread," said the people from the town.

"And for dessert," said the moose, "will you have fresh gingerbread or *apple jacquette*?"

"What do you recommend?" asked the people from the town.

"After the *chaudière de clam*, the gingerbread is best."

"Thank you," said the people from the town.

"It is my pleasure to serve you," said the moose. He brought bowls of chowder balanced on his antlers.

At the end of the meal, the moose clumped to the table. "Has everything been to your satisfaction?"

"Yup," said the people from the town, their mouths full of gingerbread.

"I beg your pardon?" said the moose. "What did you say?"

"It was very good," said the people from the town. "It was the best we've ever eaten."

59

"I will tell the chef," said the moose.

The moose clumped into the kitchen and told Mr. Breton what the people from the town had said. Mr. Breton rushed out of the kitchen and out of the house. The people from the town were sitting on the porch, putting on their snowshoes. "Did you tell the moose that my clam chowder was the best you've ever eaten?" Mr. Breton asked.

"Yup," said the people from the town. "We said that. We think that you are the best cook in the world. We have always thought so."

"Always?" asked Mr. Breton.

"Of course," the people from the town said. "Why do you think we walk seven miles on snowshoes just to eat here?"

The people from the town walked away on their snowshoes. Mr. Breton sat on the edge of the porch and thought it over. When the moose came out to see why Mr. Breton was sitting outside without his coat on, Mr. Breton said, "Do you know, those people think I am the best cook in the whole world?"

"Of course they do," the moose said. "By the way, aren't you cold out here?"

"No, I'm not the least bit cold," Mr. Breton said. "This is turning out to be a very mild winter."

When spring finally came, the moose became moody. He spent a lot of time staring out the back door. Flocks of geese flew overhead, returning to lakes in the north, and the moose always stirred when he heard their honking.

"Chef," said the moose one morning, "I will be going tomorrow. I wonder if you would pack some gingerbread for me to take along."

61

Mr. Breton baked a special batch of gingerbread, packed it in parcels, and tied the parcels with string so the moose could hang them from his antlers. When the moose came downstairs, Mr. Breton was sitting in the kitchen, drinking coffee. The parcels of gingerbread were on the kitchen table.

"Do you want a bowl of coffee before you go?" Mr. Breton asked.

"Thank you," said the moose.

"I shall certainly miss you," Mr. Breton said.

"Thank you," said the moose.

"You are my best friend," said Mr. Breton.

"Thank you," said the moose.

"Do you suppose you'll ever come back?" asked Mr. Breton.

"Not before Thursday or Friday," said the moose. "It would be impolite to visit my uncle for less than a week." The moose hooked his antlers into the loops of string on the parcels of gingerbread. "My uncle will like this." He stood up and turned toward the door.

"Wait!" Mr. Breton shouted. "Do you mean that you are not leaving forever? I thought you were lonely for the life of a wild moose. I thought you wanted to go back to the wild, free places."

"Chef, do you have any idea how cold it gets in the wild, free places?" the moose said. "And the food! Terrible!"

"Have a nice time at your uncle's," said Mr. Breton.

"I'll send you a postcard," said the moose.

Some People

Isn't it strange some people make
    You feel so tired inside,
Your thoughts begin to shrivel up
    Like leaves all brown and dried!

But when you're with some other ones,
    It's stranger still to find
Your thoughts as thick as fireflies
    All shiny in your mind!

—Rachel Field

63

An Interrupted Friendship

GILBERT GRAIL

June was a hot month in Philadelphia in 1776. The delegates to the Continental Congress were trying to decide about independence. The Revolutionary War had been going on for a year. Should the colonies now declare themselves independent of England?

In the sweltering heat, the delegate from Pennsylvania warned against such "a terrible leap into the dark." If independence were declared, the tiny new country, without friends or allies, would have to defeat England, the most powerful country in the world. Who were these delegates who would dare suggest such a step? the Pennsylvanian demanded.

Two of them were forty-year-old John Adams of Massachusetts and thirty-three-year-old Thomas Jefferson of Virginia. Both men firmly believed in independence.

Adams and Jefferson were appointed to a committee that was to draw up a declaration of independence and present it to the Continental Congress on July 1. Working late into the hot summer nights, Jefferson wrote the declaration. He then showed it to Adams and to Benjamin Franklin, another committee member. They made several changes before presenting it to the Congress. It was hotly debated, but on July 4, 1776, the Congress voted to accept the Declaration of Independence.

And so began a new nation—and a friendship that was to last, on and off, for fifty years. Jefferson had quickly grown to admire Adams's honesty and courage, and Adams recognized the Virginian's integrity and brilliant mind.

The war dragged on for another six years. The friends never saw one another, but kept in touch through letters. Adams was sent to France to assist Benjamin Franklin in getting help from that country. Then he was sent to Holland to obtain a loan for the new United States. Jefferson became the governor of Virginia, and later returned to Philadelphia as a congressman.

When the war finally ended, Adams was again in France. He helped to write the peace treaty with England. Jefferson was in Philadelphia, setting up the national system of money which we still use today. It was he who thought of the dollar as the basic unit of our money.

In the summer of 1784, Jefferson was sent to France to work with Adams and Franklin in arranging trade treaties. Eight years had gone by since the three men had worked together on the Declaration of Independence. Abigail Adams, John's wife, helped Jefferson get acquainted with French ways. Soon he replaced Franklin as the United States ambassador to France. Then Adams was appointed as our first ambassador to England, so the Adamses moved to London.

Jefferson went to London in the spring of 1786 to work with Adams on more trade treaties. He stayed for seven weeks. When they had finished their work, the two friends took a trip around the country. They visited Oxford University, Shakespeare's birthplace, Kew Gardens, and several historic battlefields. At one of the battlefields, they noticed some farm workers sitting under a tree. Adams could not resist making a speech about the battle that had taken place there. But Jefferson observed that the workers were not very impressed by his friend's speech.

Jefferson's wife had died when his daughter Polly was a baby. Now Jefferson missed Polly very much and arranged for her to join him in France. The eight-year-old girl crossed the Atlantic in 1787. She was met in London by Abigail Adams. The two became very fond of each other and Jefferson was never to forget Mrs. Adams's great kindness to the motherless Polly.

Polly became so fond of the Adamses that she wanted to stay with them. Jefferson sent a servant to bring her, reluctantly, to him in France. When she finally arrived, she told her father, "If you pick me up, I shall cry."

"If I don't, I shall cry," he told her, and soon they were once more the best of friends.

France was in a state of unrest. Soon that country's own revolution began, a revolution with which Jefferson was sympathetic. Across the Atlantic, George Washington had become the first American president, and Adams was called home to be his vice-president. Shortly after, Jefferson was named Washington's secretary of state.

The first rift in the friendship now developed. Jefferson was much in favor of the French Revolution, Adams was very opposed. Adams believed that a small well-to-do group should run the government. Jefferson believed it should be a government of all the people. Each accused the other of unfairness. Before the end of Washington's presidency, the two old friends had become enemies.

In 1796, Adams and Jefferson ran against each other for the presidency. The vote was very close. Adams became the new president, and Jefferson was the vice-president. As president, Adams had laws passed which Jefferson thought were very unwise. In 1800, the two again opposed each other for the presidency. This time, Jefferson won.

When Jefferson was sworn in as the third president, Adams did not come to the ceremony. He sincerely thought that his former friend was going to wreck the country. He was wrong. Jefferson was an able president, and the country prospered. He served eight years and then retired to Monticello, his beautiful home in Virginia.

While Jefferson was president, his beloved daughter Polly had died. She had been only twenty-five years old, and her death was a terrible blow. Polly's old friend, Abigail Adams, wrote a warm-hearted letter, giving the president her sympathy. But the rift between John Adams and Thomas Jefferson was too wide to be mended then.

Jefferson enjoyed his retirement and his grandchildren, who lived at Monticello with him. He now had time to read a lot. He looked after his large estate. He worked on his many inventions. But, as the years went by, he missed John Adams more and more.

Up in Massachusetts, Adams missed him too. Historians came to see him for firsthand information on the early years of the nation. In reliving those years, Adams thought often of the work he and Jefferson had done together. Friends of both men tried to persuade them to reestablish their old relationship.

Finally, on New Year's Day in 1811, John Adams sat down and wrote a brief letter to his old friend. Jefferson was delighted and wrote back that the letter "calls up recollections very dear to my mind." Adams was now seventy-five and Jefferson almost sixty-eight. For the next fifteen years, they wrote to each other often.

In 1818, Adams reported the sad news of Abigail's death. Jefferson replied with a touching letter. Adams was deeply moved and wrote, "I seem to have a bank at Monticello on which I can draw for a letter of friendship when I please."

On July 4, 1826, the fiftieth anniversary of the Declaration of Independence was celebrated in all of the twenty-four states. Both Adams and Jefferson had been invited to celebrations but were too ill to accept. Early in the afternoon, John Adams died at his Massachusetts home. His last words were, "Thomas Jefferson still lives." But his great friend had died at Monticello an hour before.

Thanksgiving

NICHOLASA MOHR

In early October, after we had all settled into our class and gotten used to the routine of school once more, Miss Lovett told us that this year our class was going to put on a play for Thanksgiving. The play we were going to perform was based on a poem, by Henry Wadsworth Longfellow, called "The Courtship of Miles Standish." It was about the Pilgrims and how they lived when they first landed in America.

We were all excited about the play. Miss Lovett called for volunteers to help with the sets and costumes. Paquito and I agreed to help with the sets. Consuela was going to work on makeup. Gigi had not volunteered for anything. When we asked her what she was going to do, she shrugged and didn't answer.

Miss Lovett said we could all audition for the different parts in the play. I was really interested in being Priscilla. She is the heroine. Both Captain Miles Standish and the handsome, young John Alden are in love with her. She is the most beautiful maiden in Plymouth, Massachusetts. That's where the Pilgrims used to live. I told my friends how much I would like to play that part. Everyone said I would be perfect . . . except Gigi. She said that it was a hard part to do and that maybe I wouldn't be able to play it. I really got annoyed and asked her what she meant.

"I just don't think you are right to play Priscilla. That's all," she said.

"What do you mean by 'right'?" I asked, but Gigi only shrugged and didn't say another word. She was beginning to get on my nerves.

Auditions for the parts were going to start Tuesday. Lots of kids had volunteered to audition. Paquito said he would try out for the brave Captain Miles Standish. Consuela said she was too afraid to get up in front of everybody and make a fool of herself. Gigi didn't show any interest in the play and refused to even talk to us about it. Finally the day came for the girls to read for the part of Priscilla. I was so excited I could hardly wait. Miss Lovett had given us some lines to study. I had practiced really hard. She called out all the names of those who were going to read. I was surprised when I heard her call out, "Georgina Mercado." I didn't even know Gigi wanted to try out for Priscilla. I looked at Gigi, but she ignored me. We began reading. It was my turn. I was very nervous and kept forgetting my lines. I had to look down at the script a whole lot. Several other girls were almost as nervous as I was. Then it was Gigi's turn. She recited the part almost by heart. She hardly looked at the script. I noticed that she was wearing one of her best dresses. She had never looked that good in school before. When she finished, everybody clapped. It was obvious that she was the best one. Miss Lovett made a fuss.

"You were just wonderful, Georgina," she said, "made for the part!" Boy, would I have liked another chance. I bet I could have done better than Gigi.

Why hadn't she told me she wanted the part? It's a free country, after all. She could read for the same part as I did. I wasn't going to stop her! I was really angry at Gigi.

After school everyone was still making a fuss over her. I decided I wasn't walking home with them.

"I have to meet my brothers down by the next street," I said. "I'm splitting. See you." They hardly noticed. Only Consuela said goodbye. The rest just kept on hanging all over Gigi. Big deal, I thought.

Just before all the casting was completed, Miss Lovett offered me a part as one of the Pilgrim women. All I had to do was stand in the background like a zombie. It wasn't even a speaking part.

"I don't get to say one word," I protested.

"Felicidad Maldonado, you are designing the stage sets, and you're assistant stage manager. I think that's quite a bit. Besides, all the speaking parts are taken."

"I'm not interested, thank you," I answered.

"You know"—Miss Lovett shook her head—"you can't be the best in everything."

I turned and left. I didn't need to play any part at all. Who cared?

73

The play was going to be performed on the day before Thanksgiving. I made the drawings for most of the scenery. I made a barn, a church, trees and grass, cows, and a horse. I helped the others make a real scarecrow. We used a broom and old clothes. Paquito didn't get the part of Captain Miles Standish, but he made a wonderful fence out of cardboard. It looked just like a real wooden fence. Consuela brought in her mother's old leftover makeup. She did a good job of making up everybody.

By the time we set up the stage, everything looked beautiful. Gigi had tried to talk to me a few times, but I just couldn't be nice back to her. She acted as though nothing had happened, as if I was supposed to forget she hadn't told me she was going to read for the part! I wasn't going to forget that just because she was now Miss Popularity. She could go and stay with all her newfound friends for all I cared!

The play was a tremendous hit. Everybody looked wonderful and played their parts really well. The stage was brilliant with the color I had used on my drawings. The background of the countryside, the barn, and just about everything stood out clearly. Ernesto Bratter, the stage manager, said I was a good assistant. I was glad to hear that because a couple of times I'd had to control my temper on account of his ordering me around, but it had all worked out great.

No doubt about it. Gigi was perfect as Priscilla. Even though the kids clapped and cheered for the entire cast, Gigi got more applause than anybody else. She just kept on taking a whole lot of bows.

Afterward Miss Lovett had a party for our class. We had lots of treats. There was even a record player, and we all danced. We had a really good time.

Of course, Priscilla, alias Gigi, was the big star. She just couldn't get enough attention. But not from me—that was for sure. After the party Gigi spoke to me.

"Your sets were really great. Everybody said the stage looked wonderful."

"Look," I said, interrupting her, "I gotta go. I promised my mother I'd get home early. We have to go someplace."

I rushed all the way home. I didn't know why, but I was still furious at Gigi. What was worse was that I was unhappy about having those feelings. Gigi and I had been close for as far back as I could remember. Not being able to share things with her really bothered me.

We had a great Thanksgiving. The dinner was just delicious. Afterwards, I went home with Abuelita, my grandmother. We had more of her fantastic *flan*—egg custard—and I told her all about the play. Abuelita noticed that I didn't sound too happy about Gigi's playing the part of Priscilla.

"May I ask what happened?" she said.

"Well, it's hard to explain, but what she did wasn't really fair."

"Fair about what, Felita?"

"Well, we all tried out for the different parts. Everybody knew what everybody was trying out for, but Gigi never told anybody she was going to try out for Priscilla. She kept it a great big secret. Even after I told her that I wanted to try for the part, she kept quiet about it. Do you know what she did say? She said I wasn't right for it . . . it was a hard part and all that bunch of baloney. She just wanted the part for herself, so she was mysterious about the whole thing. Like . . . it was . . . I don't know." I stopped for a moment, trying to figure this whole thing out. "After all, I am supposed to be her best friend . . . her very best friend. Why shouldn't she let me know that she wanted to be Priscilla? I wouldn't care. I let her know my plans. I didn't go sneaking around."

"Are you angry because Gigi got the part?"

It was hard for me to answer. I thought about it for a little while. "Abuelita, I don't think so. She was really good in the part."

"Were you as good when you tried out for Priscilla?"

"No." I looked at Abuelita. "I stunk." We both laughed.

"Then maybe you are not angry at Gigi at all."

76

"What do you mean?"

"Well, maybe you are a little bit . . . hurt?"

"Hurt?" I felt confused.

"Do you know what I think? I think you are hurt because your best friend didn't trust you. From what you tell me, you trusted her, but she didn't have faith in you. What do you think?"

"Yes." I nodded. "Abuelita, yes. I don't know why. Gigi and I always tell each other everything. Why did she act like that to me?"

"Have you asked her?"

"No."

"Why not? Aren't you two speaking to each other?"

"We're speaking. Gigi tried to be friendly a few times."

"Don't you want to stay her friend?"

"I do. Only she came over to me acting like . . . as if nothing had happened. Well, something did happen! What does she think? That she can go around being sneaky and I'm going to fall all over her? Just because she got the best part, she thinks she's special."

"And you think that's why she came over—because she wants to be special?"

"I don't know."

"You should give her a chance. Perhaps Gigi acted in a strange way for a reason."

"She wasn't nice to me, Abuelita. She wasn't."

"I'm not saying she was—or even that she was right. *Mira*, Felita, friendship is one of the best things in this whole world. It's one of the few things you can't go out and buy. It's like love. You can buy clothes, food, even luxuries, but there's no place I know of where you can buy a real friend. Do you?"

77

I shook my head. Abuelita smiled at me and waited. We were both silent for a long moment. I wondered if maybe I shouldn't have a talk with Gigi. After all, she had tried to talk to me first.

"Abuelita, do you think it's a good idea for me to . . . maybe talk to Gigi?"

"You know, that's a very good idea." Abuelita nodded.

I kept thinking of what Abuelita had said, and on Monday I waited for Gigi after school. It was as if she knew I wanted to talk. She came over to me.

"Hello, Gigi," I said. "How are you?"

"Fine." Gigi smiled. "Wanna walk home together?"

"Let's take the long way so we can be by ourselves," I said.

We walked without saying anything for a couple of blocks. Finally I spoke.

"I wanted to tell you, Gigi, you were really great as Priscilla."

"Did you really like me? Oh, Felita, I'm so glad. I wanted you to like me, more than anybody else. Of course, it was nothing compared to the sets you did. They were something special. Everybody liked them so much!"

"You were right too," I said. "I wasn't very good for the part of Priscilla."

"Look." Gigi stopped walking and looked at me. "I'm sorry about . . . about the way I acted. Like, I didn't say anything to you or the others. Well, I was scared you all would think I was silly or something. I mean, you wanted the part too. So, I figured, better not say anything."

"I wouldn't have cared, Gigi. Honest."

"Felita . . . it's just that you are so good at a lot of things. Like, you draw just fantastic. You beat everybody at hopscotch and kick-the-can. You know about nature and animals, much more than the rest of us. Everything you do is always better than . . . what I do! I just wanted this part for me. I wanted to be better than you this time. For once I didn't wanna worry about you. Felita, I'm sorry."

I was shocked. I didn't know Gigi had felt that way. I didn't feel better than anybody about anything I did. She looked really upset, as if she was about to cry any minute. I could see she was miserable, and I wanted to comfort her. I had never had this kind of feeling before in my whole life.

"Well, you didn't have to worry. 'Cause I stunk!" We both laughed with relief. "I think I was the worst one!"

"Oh, no, you weren't." Gigi laughed. "Jenny Fuentes was the most awful."

"Worse than I was?"

"Much worse."

It was so much fun—Gigi and I talking about the play and how we felt about everybody and everything. It was just like before, only better.

The Bat, the Birds, and the Beasts

AESOP

A great battle between the birds and the beasts was about to start. The two armies had already gathered, but the bat was having trouble deciding which to join.

The birds that passed his perch said, "Come with us." But he said, "I am a beast." Later on, some beasts who were passing underneath him looked up and said, "Come with us." But he said, "I am a bird."

Luckily peace was made between the animals at the last moment. No battle took place. The bat came to the birds and wanted to join in their celebration. But they all turned against him and he had to fly away. He then went to the beasts. But none of them would let him take part in their celebrations. Some even threatened to tear him to pieces. So he flew off alone.

"Ah," said the bat, "I see now, *he that is neither one thing nor the other has no friends.*"

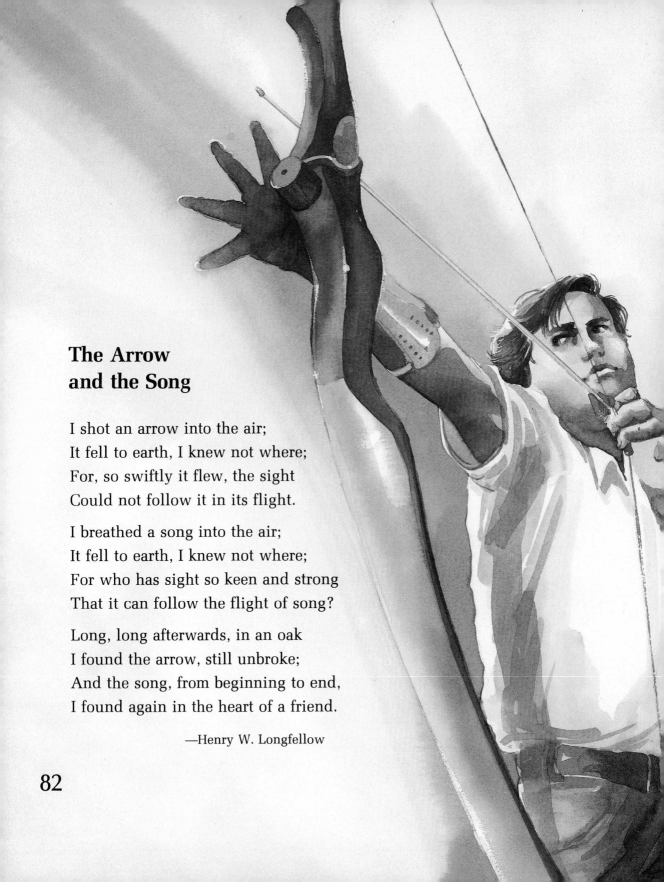

The Arrow
and the Song

I shot an arrow into the air;
It fell to earth, I knew not where;
For, so swiftly it flew, the sight
Could not follow it in its flight.

I breathed a song into the air;
It fell to earth, I knew not where;
For who has sight so keen and strong
That it can follow the flight of song?

Long, long afterwards, in an oak
I found the arrow, still unbroke;
And the song, from beginning to end,
I found again in the heart of a friend.

—Henry W. Longfellow

82

Zuckerman's Special Pig

E. B. WHITE

A pig named Wilbur, a spider named Charlotte, and a rat named Templeton are a few of the animals who live in the Zuckermans' barn. When Wilbur learned that he was being fattened up to be killed, he was very upset. Charlotte has promised to save his life.

The first step in Charlotte's plan was to weave the words "Some Pig" into a web over Wilbur's head. The Zuckermans and their hired man, Lurvy, think the appearance of the words in the web is a miracle and that Wilbur must be a special pig indeed.

One evening, a few days after the writing had appeared in Charlotte's web, the spider called a meeting of all the animals in the barn cellar.

"I shall begin by calling the roll. Wilbur?"

"Here!" said the pig.

"Gander?"

"Here, here, here!" said the gander.

"You sound like three ganders," muttered Charlotte. "Why can't you just say 'here'? Why do you have to repeat everything?"

"It's my idio-idio-idiosyncrasy," replied the gander.

"Goose?" said Charlotte.

"Here, here, here!" said the goose. Charlotte glared at her.

"Goslings, one through seven?"

"Bee-bee-bee!" "Bee-bee-bee!" "Bee-bee-bee!" "Bee-bee-bee!" "Bee-bee-bee!" "Bee-bee-bee!" "Bee-bee-bee!" said the goslings.

"This is getting to be quite a meeting," said Charlotte.
"Anybody would think we had three ganders, three geese,
and twenty-one goslings. Sheep?"

"He-aa-aa!" answered the sheep all together.

84

"Lambs?"

"He-aa-aa!" answered the lambs all together.

"Templeton?"

No answer.

"Templeton?"

No answer.

"Well, we are all here except the rat," said Charlotte. "I guess we can proceed without him. Now, all of you must have noticed what's been going on around here the last few days. The message I wrote in my web, praising Wilbur, has been received. The Zuckermans have fallen for it, and so has everybody else. Zuckerman thinks Wilbur is an unusual pig, and therefore he won't want to kill him and eat him. I dare say my trick will work and Wilbur's life can be saved."

"Hurray!" cried everybody.

"Thank you very much," said Charlotte. "Now I called this meeting in order to get suggestions. I need new ideas for the web. People are already getting sick of reading the words 'Some Pig!' If anybody can think of another message, or remark, I'll be glad to weave it into the web. Any suggestions for a new slogan?"

"How about 'Pig Supreme'?" asked one of the lambs.

"No good," said Charlotte. "It sounds like a rich dessert."

"How about 'Terrific, terrific, terrific'?" asked the goose.

"Cut that down to one 'terrific' and it will do very nicely," said Charlotte. "I think 'terrific' might impress Zuckerman."

"But Charlotte," said Wilbur, "I'm *not* terrific."

"That doesn't make a particle of difference," replied Charlotte. "Not a particle. People believe almost anything they see in print. Does anybody here know how to spell 'terrific'?"

85

"I think," said the gander, "it's tee double ee double rr double rr double eye double ff double eye double see see see see see."

"What kind of an acrobat do you think I am?" said Charlotte in disgust. "I would have to have St. Vitus's Dance to weave a word like that into my web."

"Sorry, sorry, sorry," said the gander.

Then the oldest sheep spoke up. "I agree that there should be something new written in the web if Wilbur's life is to be saved. And if Charlotte needs help in finding words, I think she can get it from our friend Templeton. The rat visits the dump regularly and has access to old magazines. He can tear out bits of advertisements and bring them up here to the barn cellar, so that Charlotte can have something to copy."

"Good idea," said Charlotte. "But I'm not sure Templeton will be willing to help. You know how he is—always looking out for himself, never thinking of the other fellow."

"I bet I can get him to help," said the old sheep. "I'll appeal to his baser instincts, of which he has plenty. Here he comes now. Everybody keep quiet while I put the matter up to him!"

The rat entered the barn the way he always did —creeping along close to the wall.

"What's up?" he asked, seeing the animals assembled.

"We're holding a directors' meeting," replied the old sheep.

"Well, break it up!" said Templeton. "Meetings bore me." And the rat began to climb a rope that hung against the wall.

"Look," said the old sheep, "next time you go to the

86

dump, Templeton, bring back a clipping from a magazine. Charlotte needs new ideas so she can write messages in her web and save Wilbur's life."

"Let him die," said the rat. "I should worry."

"You'll worry all right when next winter comes," said the sheep. "You'll worry all right on a zero morning next January when Wilbur is dead and nobody comes down here with a nice pail of warm slops to pour into the trough. Wilbur's leftover food is your chief source of supply, Templeton. *You* know that. Wilbur's food is your food; therefore Wilbur's destiny and your destiny are closely linked. If Wilbur is killed and his trough stands empty day after day, you'll grow so thin we can look right through your stomach and see objects on the other side."

Templeton's whiskers quivered.

"Maybe you're right," he said gruffly. "I'm making a trip to the dump tomorrow afternoon. I'll bring back a magazine clipping if I can find one."

"Thanks," said Charlotte. "The meeting is now adjourned. I have a busy evening ahead of me. I've got to tear my web apart and write 'Terrific.'"

Wilbur blushed. "But I'm *not* terrific, Charlotte. I'm just about average for a pig."

"You're terrific as far as *I'm* concerned," replied Charlotte, sweetly, "and that's what counts. You're my best friend, and *I* think you're sensational. Now stop arguing and go get some sleep!"

87

Far into the night, while the other creatures slept, Charlotte worked on her web. First she ripped out a few of the orb lines near the center. She left the radial lines alone, as they were needed for support. As she worked, her eight legs were a great help to her. So were her teeth. She loved to weave and she was an expert at it. When she was finished ripping things out, her web looked something like this:

A spider can produce several kinds of thread. She uses a dry, tough thread for foundation lines, and she uses a sticky thread for snare lines—the ones that catch and hold insects. Charlotte decided to use her dry thread for writing the new message.

"If I write the word 'Terrific' with sticky thread," she thought, "every bug that comes along will get stuck in it and spoil the effect."

"Now let's see, the first letter is T."

Charlotte climbed to a point at the top of the left hand side of the web. Swinging her spinnerets into position, she attached her thread and then dropped down. As she dropped, her spinning tubes went into action and she let out thread. At the bottom, she attached the thread. This formed the upright part of the Letter T. Charlotte was not satisfied, however. She climbed up and made another attachment, right next to the first. Then she carried the line down, so that she had a double line instead of a single line. "It will show up better if I make the whole thing with double lines."

She climbed back up, moved over about an inch to the left, touched her spinnerets to the web, and then carried a line across to the right, forming the top of the T. She repeated this, making it double. Her eight legs were very busy helping.

"Now for the E!"

Charlotte got so interested in her work, she began to talk to herself, as though to cheer herself on. If you had been sitting quietly in the barn cellar that evening, you would have heard something like this:

"Now for the R! Up we go! Attach! Descend! Pay out line! Whoa! Attach! Good! Up you go! Repeat! Attach! Descend! Pay out line. Whoa, girl! Steady now! Attach!

89

Climb! Attach! Over to the right! Pay out line! Attach! Now right and down and swing that loop and around and around! Now in to the left! Attach! Climb! Repeat! O.K.! Easy, keep those lines together! Now, then, out and down for the leg of the R! Pay out line! Whoa! Attach! Ascend! Repeat! Good girl!"

And so, talking to herself, the spider worked at her difficult task. When it was completed, she felt hungry. She ate a small bug that she had been saving. Then she slept.

Next morning, Wilbur arose and stood beneath the web. He breathed the morning air into his lungs. Drops of dew, catching the sun, made the web stand out clearly. When Lurvy arrived with breakfast, there was the handsome pig, and over him, woven neatly in block letters, was the word TERRIFIC. Another miracle.

Lurvy rushed and called Mr. Zuckerman. Mr. Zuckerman rushed and called Mrs. Zuckerman. Mrs.

90

Zuckerman ran to the phone and called the Arables. The Arables climbed into their truck and hurried over.

Everybody stood at the pigpen and stared at the web and read the word, over and over, while Wilbur, who really *felt* terrific, stood quietly swelling out his chest and swinging his snout from side to side.

"Terrific!" breathed Zuckerman, in joyful admiration. "Edith, you better phone the reporter on the *Weekly Chronicle* and tell him what has happened. He will want to know about this. He may want to bring a photographer. There isn't a pig in the whole state that is as terrific as our pig."

The news spread. People who had journeyed to see Wilbur when he was "some pig" came back again to see him now that he was "terrific."

That afternoon, when Mr. Zuckerman went to milk the cows and clean out the tie-ups, he was still thinking about what a wondrous pig he owned.

"Lurvy!" he called. "There is to be no more cow manure thrown down into that pigpen. I have a terrific pig. I want that pig to have clean, bright straw every day for his bedding. Understand?"

"Yes, sir," said Lurvy.

"Furthermore," said Mr. Zuckerman, "I want you to start building a crate for Wilbur. I have decided to take the pig to the County Fair on September sixth. Make the crate large and paint it green with gold letters!"

"What will the letters say?" asked Lurvy.

"They should say *Zuckerman's Famous Pig*."

Lurvy picked up a pitchfork and walked away to get some clean straw. Having such an important pig was going to mean plenty of extra work, he could see that.

The Story of Pauline

MARGARET DAVIDSON

One day some people from an oceanarium sailed out to sea looking for dolphins. They caught one and named her Pauline.

As soon as they slipped Pauline into the huge water tank at the oceanarium, they knew something was wrong. She couldn't—or wouldn't—swim. She would sink to the bottom of the tank. A doctor examined her, but could find nothing wrong. "She'll probably be all right when she gets used to the tank," he said.

But meanwhile Pauline had to breathe. How could they keep her from sinking to the bottom? Some ropes were woven together to make a raft for her. A big glass jar was tied at each corner of the raft so that it wouldn't sink. Then they slid Pauline on top of the raft.

For two days Pauline drifted around the tank on her raft. She could breathe, but she would not eat. Sometimes she whistled a high sharp whistle. This was Pauline's distress whistle. It was her way of crying "Help!" But nobody whistled back.

Once more the doctor examined her. "I still don't know what's wrong," he said. "But I do know one thing. If she doesn't begin eating soon, she'll die."

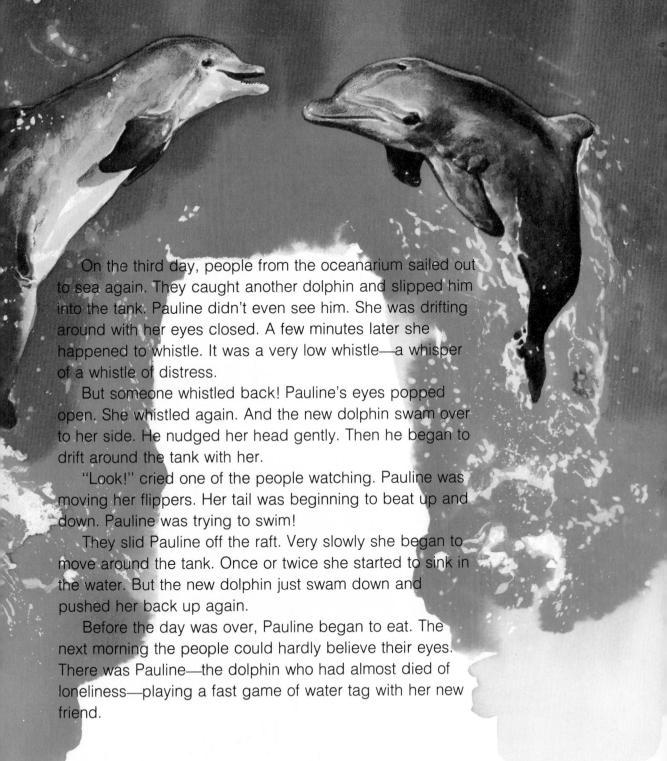

On the third day, people from the oceanarium sailed out to sea again. They caught another dolphin and slipped him into the tank. Pauline didn't even see him. She was drifting around with her eyes closed. A few minutes later she happened to whistle. It was a very low whistle—a whisper of a whistle of distress.

But someone whistled back! Pauline's eyes popped open. She whistled again. And the new dolphin swam over to her side. He nudged her head gently. Then he began to drift around the tank with her.

"Look!" cried one of the people watching. Pauline was moving her flippers. Her tail was beginning to beat up and down. Pauline was trying to swim!

They slid Pauline off the raft. Very slowly she began to move around the tank. Once or twice she started to sink in the water. But the new dolphin just swam down and pushed her back up again.

Before the day was over, Pauline began to eat. The next morning the people could hardly believe their eyes. There was Pauline—the dolphin who had almost died of loneliness—playing a fast game of water tag with her new friend.

93

I'll Tell Emily

I'm going to pet a worm today
I'm going to pet a worm—don't *say*
Don't pet a worm, I'm doing it soon—
Emily's coming this afternoon!
And you know what she'll probably say
I touched a mouse or
I held a snake or
I felt a dead bird's wing
And she'll turn to me with a kind of smile
What did you *do that's interesting*?
This time
I am
Going to say
Why, Emily, you should have seen me
pet a worm today!
And I'll tell her he stretched and he shrunk like elastic
And I got a chill and it felt fantastic
And I'll see her smile fade away when she
Wishes that moment she could be me!

—Constance Levy

Unit Three
Beginnings

Prometheus

Greek Myth

At the beginning of the world, trees and grass began to grow on the earth. The animals were created, but not humans. Horses roamed the plains, monkeys played in the trees, and bears lived peacefully in the forest. Cats lay in the sun all day and padded through the wet grass at night. Fish leaped in the rivers and oceans. Birds built their nests.

A giant god named Prometheus and his brother, Epimetheus, guarded the animals as they came to life. It was the duty of Epimetheus to give each newly created animal a gift to help it survive in the new world. He gave wings to the birds, claws to the tiger, shells to the turtles. The lion was given strength, the fox cunning, and the deer speed.

But Prometheus thought there was need for an animal nobler than any of the beasts of the plain and the forest. One day as he was resting on the shore, Prometheus scooped up a handful of earth. He moistened the earth with water from the ocean, and fashioned it into a statue in the image of the gods. The sun warmed the statue and the sea breezes cooled it. The earth of the statue began to change into new colors and the image came to life. Prometheus called this new being a human.

Because the human was made in the image of the gods, Prometheus asked Epimetheus for a gift finer than any he had given the other animals. Epimetheus was sorry but he had just given away the last gift and had nothing special left to give to the human. He and Prometheus discussed the problem. Where could they find a suitable gift?

They asked Athena, the goddess of wisdom, for help. She
suggested that Prometheus look on Mount Olympus, the
home of the gods. He followed her advice and went high into
the sky, beyond the clouds, to the heavenly mountain. After
much searching, Prometheus decided on a gift. He dipped
his torch into the fire of the gods, taking great care not to be
seen. He then descended quickly to earth and handed the
torch to the human. So humans received the finest gift of all,
fire.

97

When the other gods learned that Prometheus had stolen fire from Mount Olympus, some of them were enraged. These gods said that by giving humans this great gift, Prometheus had made them too powerful. Zeus, the ruler of the gods, ordered that Prometheus be chained to a rock high on Mount Caucasus. There he would be exposed to the burning sun and left at the mercy of a fierce vulture for all eternity.

Prometheus accepted his punishment. He willingly sacrificed himself for the humans he had created and to whom he had given fire.

Soon there were more humans. With fire, they heated metals and formed weapons to protect themselves. They made tools to cultivate the fields and built fires to heat their homes. Fire enabled humans to do things that other animals could not do, and they became the rulers of the world.

Trina

PATRICIA MILES MARTIN

Trina can read, write, and understand English, but she can't speak it or read it aloud. Whenever she tries, her words come out in Spanish.

On her first day of school this year, Trina felt embarrassed and ashamed. Her brother, Jaime, spoke for her when the teacher asked her name. And when the teacher asked her a question, she couldn't think of the English words to use for the answer. She couldn't even read aloud out of a reader she knew by heart. So Trina has decided that she will not go back to school until she can speak English as well as her brother.

"Each day the teacher calls your name and no one answers," Jaime said late one afternoon. "Each day the teacher asks why you are not in school and I say nothing."

"And how does it happen that you say nothing?" Trina asked. "Always, when I am there, you speak for me. You don't wait to let me talk. You say something. Anything. You say, 'Trina can't read.' "

She started after him and he retreated, yelling loudly, "Mama, Trina's starting a fight. Mama!"

"This is enough," Mama said. "Let me hear no more."

Trina ran outside and looked up the hill. Some of the boys were playing ball across the street from the hotel, and on the hotel veranda two men sat on a bench feeding the goat.

Trina recognized Mr. Green's horse and buggy standing near the tracks. Mr. Green must have stopped there to watch the train go by. The reins were slack, and old Ruby grazed beside the fence. The buggy was turned toward the pasture.

As Trina started off toward the depot, the horse ambled a little way and stopped to reach down for a clump of grass. The wheels of the buggy now rested on the tracks. Something was wrong.

Trina ran toward the buggy calling, "Señor Green. Señor Green."

When she reached the buggy, it was empty. Far away the train whistle blew. Trina ran to old Ruby's head and pulled at the bridle.

"*Ruby*," Trina said. "*¡Anda, anda!*"

The whistle was louder. Ruby snorted ill-naturedly and jerked her head out of reach. The horse didn't understand Spanish. "Gitty up, gitty up," Trina shouted in English.

There was shouting from the hotel, and Trina's mother called her name. Ruby lowered her head again, and Trina grabbed the bridle and tugged. "Ven, ven. Come on, Ruby. *¡Ahora!* At once." Trina could hear the rumble of the train and the frantic whistle.

The horse ambled forward. The wheels caught against the tracks, and they thumped across, rocking the buggy from side to side. Ruby and buggy were safe over the tracks.

The train came hissing, wheels sliding. It stopped in front of the station. The conductor and the brakeman ran back alongside the train.

Trina's mother had come down to the tracks, and people were coming from every direction.

"What's going on here?" the conductor asked. "Don't you know you could have caused a train wreck with that horse on the track? And the horse would have been killed too. Who let you bring that horse down here?"

Trina couldn't answer—not even in Spanish.

People came running down the hill. "She didn't bring the buggy here," someone said. "That's Green's horse."

"That's my horse," Mr. Green said. He could hardly talk. "I left her standing in front of the store."

"That little girl got the horse off the tracks," a man said.

The conductor shoved his cap toward the back of his head. "Whew! I haven't had such a scare in years. I thought we'd hit that horse." He patted Trina's shoulder. "You're a very smart girl."

When the train pulled out, the engineer blew his whistle. Trina knew that he blew it just for her.

"Bring your mother and come with me," Mr. Green said. He helped her mother into the buggy, and Trina climbed up beside her. Mr. Green talked all the way up the hill.

"When I looked out and saw that Ruby was gone, I thought at first she'd only wandered off a few steps, and then when I saw where she was, I started running. When that train whistle blew, I knew I didn't have a chance. Then I saw Trina."

Boys and girls were running along beside the buggy, laughing and shoving each other. The teacher came hurrying from the hotel.

Quite a crowd gathered while Mr. Green tied Ruby to the hitching rail. "I'll never trust her again," he said. "She gets tied after this."

Inside the store he led Trina to a glass counter. Behind the glass were many toys. "You may have whichever you want," said Mr. Green. "You choose."

Trina looked at all the toys. She pointed to a brightly-colored ball.

"*Me gusta,*" she said. "I like it."

"It's yours," Mr. Green said.

"I wish I'd been there when old Ruby stopped on the tracks," Jaime said.

"Trina's lucky," Ricardo said.

"Our town's lucky," Mr. Green corrected him.

104

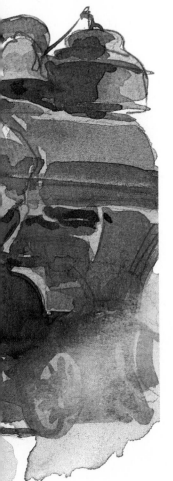

"Trina's not the lucky one. The town's lucky to have a girl as brave as Trina growing up in it."

"Trina spoke English to old Ruby when the train was coming," Flavio Valdez said. "Did you know, Trina? I heard you."

Trina shook her head.

Then the teacher had an arm around Trina's shoulder and was giving her a hug. "I need to have you back at school," the teacher said. "We all need you."

Trina tried to speak. One of these days soon all the English words that she needed would come, and when they did, Trina would talk a lot, for she had so much to say.

The teacher was still smiling. "Perhaps I didn't give you time enough to answer? Perhaps I didn't wait long enough? Will you come back to school tomorrow and give me another chance? Please?"

Trina nodded. Never had she been happier. *Never—so happy. Nunca tan feliz.* Her thoughts were a jumble of Spanish and English.

On the way home her mother wanted to know what had been said. When Trina told her, her mother looked pleased.

"Every day when Papa comes home from work, he and Jaime will speak English at home," she said. "And you and I will try to speak also. We will listen and learn."

Trina nodded. "Soon we will both speak English," she said cheerfully.

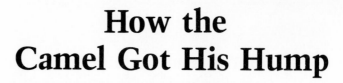

How the Camel Got His Hump

RUDYARD KIPLING

Now this tale tells how the Camel got his big hump.

In the beginning of years, when the world was so new and all, and the Animals were just beginning to work for Humans, there was a Camel, and he lived in the middle of a Howling Desert because he did not want to work. Besides, he was a Howler himself. So he ate sticks and thorns and tamarisks and milkweed and prickles, most 'scruciating idle. When anybody spoke to him he said "Humph!" Just "Humph!" and no more.

Presently the Horse came to him on Monday morning, with a saddle on his back and a bit in his mouth, and said, "Camel, O Camel, come out and trot like the rest of us."

"Humph!" said the Camel. And the Horse went away and told the Human.

Presently the Dog came to him, with a stick in his mouth, and said, "Camel, O Camel, come and fetch and carry like the rest of us."

"Humph!" said the Camel. And the Dog went away and told the Human.

Presently the Ox came to him, with the yoke on his neck and said, "Camel, O Camel, come and plow like the rest of us."

"Humph!" said the Camel. And the Ox went away and told the Human.

At the end of the day the Human called the Horse and the Dog and the Ox together, and said, "Three, O Three, I'm very sorry for you (with the world so new and all), but that

Humph-thing in the Desert can't work, or he would have been here by now. So I am going to leave him alone, and you must work double time to make up for it."

That made the Three very angry (with the world so new and all), and they held a palaver, and an *indaba*, and a *punchayet*, and a powwow on the edge of the Desert, and the Camel came chewing milkweed *most* 'scruciating idle, and laughed at them. Then he said "Humph!" and went away again.

Presently there came along the Djinn in charge of All Deserts, rolling in a cloud of dust (Djinns always travel that way because it is Magic), and he stopped to palaver and powwow with the Three.

"Djinn of All Deserts," said the Horse, "is it right for any one to be idle, with the world so new and all?"

"Certainly not," said the Djinn.

"Well," said the Horse, "there's a thing in the middle of your Howling Desert (and he's a Howler himself) with a long neck and long legs, and he hasn't done a stroke of work since Monday morning. He won't trot."

"Whew!" said the Djinn, whistling, "that's my Camel, for all the gold in Arabia! What does he say about it?"

"He says 'Humph!'" said the Dog, "and he won't fetch and carry."

"Does he say anything else?"

"Only 'Humph!', and he won't plow," said the Ox.

"Very good," said the Djinn. "I'll humph him if you will kindly wait a minute."

The Djinn rolled himself up in his dustcloak and took a bearing across the desert, and found the Camel most 'scruciatingly idle, looking at his own reflection in a pool of water.

"My long and bubbling friend," said the Djinn, "what's this I hear of your doing no work, with the world so new and all?"

"Humph!" said the Camel.

The Djinn sat down, with his chin in his hand, and began to think a Great Magic, while the Camel looked at his own reflection in the pool of water.

"You've given the Three extra work ever since Monday morning, all on account of your 'scruciating idleness," said the Djinn. And he went on thinking Magics, with his chin in his hand.

"Humph!" said the Camel.

"I shouldn't say that again if I were you," said the Djinn. "You might say it once too often. Bubbles, I want you to work."

And the Camel said "Humph!" again. But no sooner had

he said it than he saw his back, that he was so proud of, puffing up and puffing up into a great big lolloping humph.

"Do you see that?" said the Djinn. "That's your very own humph that you've brought upon your very own self by not working. Today is Thursday, and you've done no work since Monday, when the work began. Now you are going to work."

"How can I," said the Camel, "with this humph on my back?"

"That's made a-purpose," said the Djinn, "all because you missed those three days. You will be able to work now for three days without eating, because you can live on your humph. And don't you ever say I never did anything for you. Come out of the Desert and go to the Three, and behave. Humph yourself!"

And the Camel humphed himself, humph and all, and went away to join the Three. And from that day to this the Camel always wears a humph (we call it "hump" now, not to hurt his feelings). But he has never yet caught up with the three days that he missed at the beginning of the world, and he has never yet learned how to behave.

Benjamin Franklin
Changes the World

ISAAC ASIMOV

The world was a cruel and frightening place to our ancestors. Nobody knew what made it work. The rain might come or not come. There might be early frosts or floods. Any number of things might spoil the crops and bring on starvation. Disease might strike suddenly and kill domestic animals, or even the people themselves.

The world seemed so puzzling that many people decided it was run by demons or spirits. To stay on the good side of the demons and keep them from getting angry, people developed ceremonies and superstitions they believed would protect them from bad luck.

Some people still have superstitions today. For example, they might knock on wood to keep bad luck away, or carry a rabbit's foot to bring good luck. Although these superstitious practices might make people feel safer, they don't really work, because they have nothing to do with the real world.

People who study how the real world works are called scientists. They try to find out such things as what causes disease, and what makes the weather behave as it does.

Modern science began about the year 1600, but for nearly one hundred fifty years, it didn't have much effect on the lives of ordinary people. Scientists, for example, found out that the earth went around the sun instead of the sun circling the earth, but that didn't make the crops grow better or keep people healthy.

110

Then in 1752, for the first time, a scientific discovery was made that affected everyday life—it saved people from a natural disaster. And that changed the world, for now many people turned to science rather than superstition to keep harm away.

You might have thought this would have happened in Europe where, in those days, science was most advanced. It didn't. It happened in Philadelphia in the American colonies.

In the early 1700s, many scientists in Europe were interested in electricity. They had found that if they rubbed rods of glass or sealing wax, the rods attracted lightweight objects such as feathers and small bits of wood. The rubbed objects were said to be "charged" with electricity.

Some devices could be charged with a great deal of electricity. One such device, studied at the University of Leyden in the Netherlands, was called a "Leyden jar." If a Leyden jar is filled with a particularly large charge of electricity, that electricity might suddenly pour out the way air pours out of a punctured balloon. When electricity pours out, or "discharges," it heats the air, causing a little spark. The air expands with the heat, then cools and contracts, all in a split second, making a little crackling sound.

In the American colonies, a scientist named Benjamin Franklin was interested in electricity and experimented with Leyden jars, too. He discovered that if he attached a small metal rod to the Leyden jar, the discharge came off the end of the rod. If the Leyden jar was charged high enough, and if something was brought near the rod, a spark would shoot off the rod, and there would be a crackle.

The thinner the rod, the quicker the discharge would come. If a very thin rod with a sharp end was used, a charge couldn't be built up in the Leyden jar at all. As fast as an electric charge was transferred into the jar, it leaked out of the sharp end of the rod. And it leaked out so quietly that there was no spark or crackle.

Some people said the spark and crackle were like tiny lightning and thunder. Franklin thought of it the other way. Could real lightning and thunder be a huge electric discharge from a cloud or from the ground?

This was an important new thought. Everyone was afraid of lightning. It struck without warning. It could set a house or a barn on fire. It could kill an animal or a human being. The ancients believed that lightning was a weapon used by the gods. The Greeks thought that Zeus hurled lightning bolts, and the Norse thought that Thor threw his fiery hammer. Now, if Franklin could find out that lightning was an electric discharge, it might be possible to understand lightning better—and fear it less.

In June, 1752, Franklin made a kite and tied a metal rod to it. He placed a metal key at the bottom end of the kite string. Then, during a thunderstorm, he went out to fly the kite, hoping to see if electricity would flow from the clouds down to the key. He didn't hold the kite string with his hand for fear the electricity would flow into him and kill him. Instead, he tied a silk thread to the string and held that, because electricity doesn't travel through silk.

When the kite vanished into a storm cloud, he carefully brought one knuckle near the key. The key discharged, producing a spark and a crackle, just as a Leyden jar would. And the spark felt the same on his knuckle as a spark from a Leyden jar.

Franklin had an uncharged Leyden jar with him. He brought it near the key, and electricity flowed from the clouds into the key and from the key into the Leyden jar. The Leyden jar was charged with electricity from the sky, but it behaved just as though the charge had been produced on earth. Franklin thought this meant that the lightning in the sky would follow the same rules that electricity on earth would.

During a thunderstorm, the ground could become filled with a charge of electricity. If it did, there might eventually be a huge discharge—a lightning bolt. If the discharge worked its way through a building, the heat could set the building on fire.

But Franklin had found that if a thin rod was attached to a Leyden jar, it wouldn't build up a charge. The electrical charge would leak out of the sharp end of the rod as quickly as it was built up, and there would be no spark. Suppose the same thing was done to a building? Suppose a thin metal rod was placed on top of a building and connected to the ground? In a thunderstorm, the ground under the building would not build up a charge because the charge would leak quietly away through the thin rod. The building would therefore not be hit by lightning.

Franklin called such a device a "lightning rod." Every year, he published an almanac in which he printed information about all sorts of things. In the 1753 edition, he described how to put a lightning rod on a house or a barn to keep it from being hit by lightning.

It was such a simple thing to do, and people were so afraid of lightning, that soon after the almanac came out, lightning rods began to be placed on houses all over the colonies. They were used in Europe, too.

And it wasn't a superstition. It worked! For the first time in history, one of the terrors of the world could be controlled—and it was science that did it. Spells and magic could be forgotten. Simply by understanding what lightning was and how electricity worked, people could take advantage of that knowledge and protect themselves.

And gradually people began to understand that science worked and superstition didn't. In 1767, for instance, the citizens of the Italian city of Brescia stored a great deal of gunpowder in the cellar of a tall building that did not have a lightning rod. They thought the gunpowder was safe there because the building was a church. But the church was struck by lightning during a storm and all the gunpowder exploded, destroying much of the city and killing three thousand people. This great tragedy ended any doubts about lightning rods.

From that time on, in many, many ways, science helped people where superstition had just fooled and confused them. In 1798, an English doctor learned how to inoculate against smallpox. That was the beginning of the victory of science over sickness. In the 1840s, doctors learned how to use certain chemicals to put patients to sleep during operations. That was the beginning of the victory of science over pain.

And these beginnings, which enabled science to help ordinary people in a practical way, owed much to a remarkable American colonial named Benjamin Franklin, who flew a kite in a thunderstorm and changed the world.

New Year's Day

Last night, while we were fast asleep,
    The old year went away.
It can't come back again because
    A new one's come to stay.

—Rachel Field

Salt Boy

MARY PERRINE

The thing Salt Boy wanted only his father could give
him. But asking for it, Salt Boy thought, might make his
father be against it. Then, one morning, he asked for it.

He was in the trees getting wood for his mother's fire
when he saw his father coming with a rope to begin the
training of the black horse.

His heart began to jump in a funny way, like a
grasshopper, and he went to the bent tree, where he
could stand not far from the black horse and watch his
father when he threw the rope.

The black horse was eating grass. Salt Boy's father
walked quietly, and the black horse didn't hear him until
he was near. Then, suddenly, its ears went up, and its
head, and it began to dance away backwards.

Still walking quietly, Salt Boy's father threw the rope.
With no sound, it went high over the black horse's ears
and slid down easily around its neck.

The black horse stood there, surprised, and shook its head as if a fly had bothered it. Keeping the rope tight, Salt Boy's father went close to the black horse, and talked to it, and stroked it with kindness. Then he untied the rope and let the black horse go.

It was then Salt Boy went to his father and, almost hiding his face with the wood in his arms, said it. "My father, will you teach me sometime to rope the black horse?"

Without answering, his father started to their hogan, and Salt Boy went behind him. Without words, they crossed the red sand of the mesa top and went down the black rocks below.

When they came to the pen for Salt Boy's mother's sheep, his father stopped and waited until Salt Boy was beside him. Then he spoke. "I have said it before, my son, that you must never rope the sheep of your mother."

Salt Boy wanted to hide the shame on his face from his father. He looked at the ground and turned a rock over with his toe. He was thinking that his father must know, then, what he had done in the canyon when he took his mother's sheep for grass.

Then his father spoke again. "Maybe, my son," he said, "when your years are more, I will teach you to rope the black horse."

Salt Boy and his father looked at each other in a way that was strong, and Salt Boy knew his father had asked without words for a promise, and without words Salt Boy had given it to him. That promise he thought he would keep.

119

In the morning, Salt Boy took his mother's sheep to the canyon for grass.

Near the wash at the bottom of the canyon the grass was green and deep, and the sheep ran to it, pushing against each other. When the sheep ran, the lamb that was littlest lost its mother and cried, "M-a-a." Salt Boy lifted it and carried it with gentleness to its mother.

There was a tall flat rock by the grass where the sheep were, and Salt Boy climbed up on it. From there he could watch the sheep, and if he turned around and leaned over, he could see the cave that held the thing that he had found.

He remembered the morning he had found it there. At first, when he saw it in the cave, he had thought it was a snake, and he had felt it with a long stick, and moved it, and turned it over. When the stick told him it was a thing without life, he had gone close to it and put his hand on it. It wasn't until then he had known it was a rope.

He had pulled it carefully and slowly out of the darkness in the cave. Then he had sat on the ground and looked at it, and felt it, and held it. He had done that with it all day, until it was time to take his mother's sheep back up the canyon path. Then he had coiled it very slowly and put it back in the cave's darkness.

After that morning he had taken the rope out of the cave many times. He had learned to tie it well, and he had learned to throw it without missing over the round gray rocks that were in the canyon.

Then, one time when the rope was in his hands and he was getting ready to throw it over a round gray rock, a sheep had come near, and suddenly he had thrown it over the sheep's head.

Now Salt Boy sat on the rock that was tall and flat. He was thinking about that first time, and he was thinking about how many times after that he had thrown the rope over the heads of other sheep of his mother. And he was thinking about yesterday and the promise he had given his father.

He might have stayed there longer, but his legs hurt from the rock that was tall and flat, and after a while he jumped to the ground. Then, without planning it, he went to the cave where the rope was hidden.

He could see it in the cave's darkness, and he leaned down to take it out. Just then a noise began coming from the sky. Black clouds were in it, and wind was coming from it. Then gray rain began to come, and soon gray rain was everywhere.

Salt Boy started to the sheep. Heavy wind stood against him, and to walk he had to hold big rocks and pull himself.

At last, that way, he came to the grass by the wash. The sheep were afraid and were standing close to one another. They were stiff, like things made from wood. Quickly Salt Boy counted—first the sheep and then the lambs. One lamb was missing! The littlest lamb was gone!

Salt Boy looked at the wash, which was near. It was full of water that was moving fast, like a strong horse running.

Something was in the water by the flat rock, and Salt Boy leaned over to see it better. It was the littlest lamb, and it was kicking and trying to stand. But it kept slipping and falling, and then the water carried it.

Salt Boy tried to go in the water to help the littlest lamb, but the wind pushed him, and he fell. To get out, he crawled on his knees.

The rope that was in the cave, he knew then, was the only way he could save the littlest lamb.

Gray rain was still coming, and wind, and he held big rocks and pulled himself until he was near the cave. He crawled to it and got the rope, and then he held big rocks and pulled himself again until he was back by the wash.

He tied the rope as fast as he could and threw it. He missed and threw again. This time it went over the head of the littlest lamb.

Salt Boy pulled the rope slowly and carefully until the littlest lamb was out of the water.

He lifted it and held it in his arms. It was lying very still, but when Salt Boy put his face close to it, he could feel the beating of its heart.

Something—maybe a sound—made him look around. His father was standing behind him. His father stayed there for a while, and then he said with quietness, "I watched, my son, while you saved the littlest lamb of your mother."

He still didn't go.

Salt Boy held the littlest lamb and waited. Then his father said, "Tomorrow, my son, I will teach you to rope the black horse."

123

Day and Night:
How They Came to Be

Eskimo Song

In those times
when just saying a word
could make something happen,
there was no light on earth yet.
Everything was in darkness all the time,
people lived in darkness.

A fox and a hare had an argument,
each saying his magic word:
"Darkness," said the fox,
for he wanted it to be dark so he could go hunting.

"Day," said the hare,
for he wanted daylight
so he could find good grass to eat.

The hare won: His word was more powerful
and he got his wish:
Day came, replacing night.
But the word of the fox was powerful too
and when day was over, night came,
and from then on they took turns with each other,
the nighttime of the fox
following the daytime of the hare.

124   —Translated by Edward Field

Memories

ELOISE GREENFIELD

Doretha was bored sitting there on the sofa with her white-casted leg stretched out. She could hear her friends outside jumping rope.

> *Mama, Mama, don't cry, don't cry,*
> *I jumped all the way to the clear blue sky,*
> *I touched the sun, but I ain't gonna die,*
> *Oh, Mama, Mama, don't cry, don't cry.*

125

Just two days ago she had been doing the same thing, jumping in and out of the rope and reaching up to touch the sun, when she landed on a rock, twisted her foot, and broke her ankle. Now here she was, stuck during the Easter holidays. She was tired of television, tired of playing jacks, tired of sitting on the porch watching her friends play. Her sister had gone out. And inside the cast, her leg itched.

"No sense in you sitting there with your mouth stuck out, Sister," her mother said. She moved the dustcloth over the dark brown wood of the secondhand piano. "Alberta's been entertaining you for two whole days, and she's got a right to go out with her friends sometime."

Doretha didn't answer. She sat slumped against the arm of the sofa. She usually enjoyed watching her mother dust the piano very carefully as if it had feelings and too hard a touch would make it cry, but today it seemed dumb. She heard a key in the door and stuck her lips out more.

"Hey, how my girls doing?" Her father was home, tall and neat in khaki pants, his short beard hiding the top of his turtleneck shirt.

"Hi, Cle." His wife left the piano and met him at the door. She reached up and touched her lips to his. "Tired?"

He shrugged and threw his jacket on the chair. "Uh-oh," he said, looking at Doretha. "Thelma, what've you been doing to my baby?"

"I didn't do a thing to her," Mrs. Freeman said. She laughed, and all three of her dimples dotted her face. Even the one Doretha called a high dimple, at the top of her right cheekbone. "Alberta went to the movies with Brenda, and your baby's feeling sorry for herself."

Doretha's father came over to her. "She sure does look mean," he said. "I bet she wouldn't laugh now if a joke walked right up and tickled her in the stomach." He tickled her side and the laughter fell out of her. "Hey, that's better. Tell you what. While I'm getting some of this dust off me, I'll try to think of something we can do, me and you and Mama. But it won't be going for a ride, I tell you that right now. I parked so many cars today, I don't want to see anything on wheels."

In a little while he was back, carrying a cardboard box.

"What's that, Daddy?" Doretha asked.

"My junk box. Stuff I had when I was in high school. Everything in here is sixteen or seventeen years old. Been saving it just for the time you'd try to beat up a rock with your big toe." He set the box on the coffee table and went to the kitchen to get two chairs.

"Come on, Thelma. We need you in here, too. Okay, Sister, you pick out what you want to look at and I'll tell you all about it."

Doretha took her time going through the things in the box, looking at pictures of her father and his friends in front of a three-story red brick building, a birthday card from a girl named Joyce, a magazine clipping of Miles Davis blowing his trumpet, and one of Jackie Robinson.

And then she saw the frayed corner of the looseleaf notebook sticking through. She lifted it out. It was large and black, and at the corners gray cardboard showed through the worn covering. On the inside of the front cover was written, "Clemont Freeman, Cardozo High School." The book was filled with yellowed lined paper, most of it unused. It looked a hundred years old to Doretha.

"Daddy!" she said. "Can I have this?"

127

"You don't want that, Sister," Mr. Freeman said. "It's probably got paper lice all over it."

"You can spray it, can't you?"

"Now, Sister," her mother said, "Cle wants to keep that. What in the world you want it for?"

"I don't know. Yet. But I'll think of something. Please, Daddy? You can take out the paper you wrote on."

"Well . . ."

"Please, Daddy?"

"Sure, honey, you can have it."

Doretha didn't have any idea what she would do with the book. But it was so old and ugly and beautiful that she had to have it. She took it to bed with her every night, and in a few days she knew how she would use it.

"Mama," she said one morning, "how do you spell memories?"

Song of Creation

I have made the sun!
  I have made the sun!
Hurling it high
  In the four directions
To the east I threw it
  To run its appointed course.

I have made the moon!
  I have made the moon!
Hurling it high
  In the four directions
To the east I threw it
  To run its appointed course.

—Pima

This Newly Created World

Pleasant it looked,
this newly created world.
Along the entire length and breadth
of the earth, our grandmother,
extended the green reflection
of her covering
and the escaping odors
were pleasant to inhale.

—Winnebago

130

Peeping in the Shell

FAITH MCNULTY

The whooping crane is a very rare bird, and for some years now scientists in North America have worked to make sure that whooping cranes will survive in the world. In this story the author has been invited to watch the hatching of a whooping crane egg in an incubator. The evening she arrives the whooping crane chick has "pipped," or poked the first tiny hole in its egg. The next morning she begins to watch the day-long process of hatching.

At nine o'clock in the morning, I went to the incubator room. Mike, the scientist in charge of the whooping crane egg, was there.

Mike said that the egg had spent a quiet night—too quiet. He was disappointed that the chick had not made more progress. I peered in the window and saw that a few bits of shell had been chipped away. The tiny hole had become a slot about a quarter of an inch long. I could faintly see something quivering in the darkness in the depths of the shell.

For the next hour I sat beside the incubator. From time to time I looked in at the egg. Sometimes I saw something moving beneath the slot, but mostly the chick was quiet.

Mike took a tray of eggs out of one of the other incubators and put it on the table in front of him. He began to pick up eggs, one by one, and make notes in his ledger.

Action! I glanced into the whooping crane incubator and saw that a bit of shell had fallen from the rim of the hole in the egg. The tip of a beak stuck out, wavered, and fell back. I called Mike. He got up and opened the door. "Hi, there!" he called in a crooning voice. A series of tiny, piping cries answered. The sound was eager and urgent, but very, very, small. For an instant the beak was thrust out of the hole.

"You're doing real good," Mike said encouragingly, and shut the door. The beak continued to poke

131

out, nod, and disappear, as though the chick were trying to reach out to us.

"How much longer will it take to hatch?" I asked.

"Lots longer," Mike replied. He explained that within the next few hours the chick should peck a line of holes circling the end of the egg. When the circle was complete, the end of the shell could be pushed off, setting the chick free. To peck a ring of holes the chick would have to turn inside the egg. Mike called this "spinning." It had been almost a day since our chick had pipped. By now it should have begun to spin.

For two more hours I sat by the incubator, looking in now and then. From time to time the chick pecked at the edges of the slot.

At intervals Mike got up, opened the door, and talked to the chick. Each time I could see its beak poke out in response, wave frantically, then disappear. I was beginning to feel anxious.

"Is he spinning?" I asked Mike as he shut the door.

"Not yet," Mike said. "Give him time. It takes an awful lot of energy to hatch."

Two more hours went by, but the slot in the egg had not grown much bigger. Though the chick pecked, it wasn't able to crack the tough shell. If the end of the egg were the face of a clock, the chick had chipped away no more than the space between twelve and one. I began to feel that the chick was in trouble and to wish Mike would do something.

After what seemed a long time, Mike opened the door again. He was greeted with frantic peeping—like cries for help.

"Hi, kid!" Mike said softly. "What's going on?" He picked up the egg and cradled it in his left hand. He gazed at it thoughtfully.

"I guess it's time to take a look," he said. "Maybe this guy isn't able to spin. Maybe something is holding him up."

With his right hand Mike picked up a pair of blunt scissors and gently nibbled at the edges of the hole, pulling away tiny bits of shell. The chick trilled excitedly. Suddenly I was able to see it—a dark shade of pinkish brown, wet and leathery. I could see toes and a beak and the quills of one wing all cramped together.

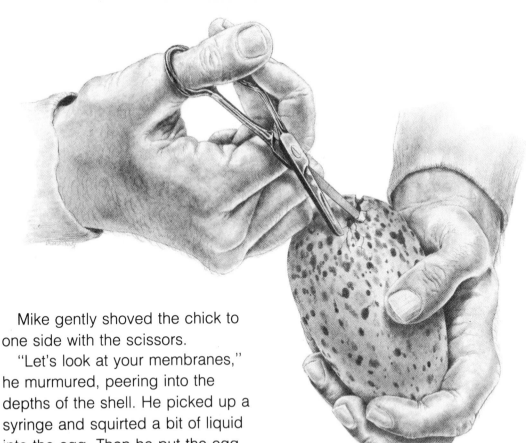

Mike gently shoved the chick to one side with the scissors.

"Let's look at your membranes," he murmured, peering into the depths of the shell. He picked up a syringe and squirted a bit of liquid into the egg. Then he put the egg back. For a few moments I could hear the chick's voice as it continued to peep. Then silence.

Mike explained that he had squirted water into the shell to wet the membranes in case they were stuck to the chick. He thought that might be the reason the chick wasn't spinning.

I asked Mike why he didn't simply pull the chick out of the shell.

It was, Mike explained, because pulling it out suddenly might kill it. During hatching, he went on, each step must take place at the proper time. While the chick is doing its work of pecking at the shell, the blood vessels that once supplied oxygen are drying up. If the chick were pulled out of the shell before these vessels had sealed themselves off, the chick might bleed to death.

Also, Mike went on, there is the yolk—a mass of concentrated food—that is pressed against the chick's underside near the tail. In another of the miraculous changes

133

of hatching, this yolk is sucked into the chick's body through its umbilical cord. After the chick hatches, the yolk provides food for a day or so until the chick is strong enough to eat. The yolk should be inside the chick, and the umbilical cord dried up, before the chick leaves the shell. Mike had seen that quite a bit of yolk had not yet been absorbed.

On the other hand, Mike explained, there is also danger if hatching takes too long. While the chick is cramped inside the shell, it cannot breathe deeply because there is not enough room for its lungs to expand fully. After a time, a shortage of oxygen combined with exhaustion can cause the chick to give up and slowly die.

I looked at our poor egg and its bravely struggling prisoner with new anxiety. The chick seemed so frail, its task so tremendous.

Three hours later there had still been no change. The chick was resting. Or was it giving up? Mike sat quietly reading a book. I wondered how he could be so calm.

By mid-afternoon I was feeling not only anxious but also weary. I was tired of the windowless basement room, the straight chair, the humming sound of the incubators, and the endless wait. I watched the chick as it quivered, struggled, and rested again and again. It didn't seem to be getting anywhere.

Mike went on reading. I sensed that he didn't want to talk about the sad possibility that the chick might die, but I had to know what he thought.

"Mike," I asked, "is this hatching still normal? I mean, hasn't it taken too long?"

Mike looked up briefly. "It's getting close," he said, and went back to reading.

At the end of the next hour there had been quite a bit of change. The chick was peeping steadily. One leathery wing was exposed, pulsing with each peep. I could see the chick's fragile skull. It was thinly covered with wet feathers like fine hair. The chick struggled steadily. Its beak waved and waved.

Mike put down his book. He got up and stared into the incubator for a long time. Then he picked up forceps—a metal tool that resembles a pair of blunt scissors.

He opened the door and placed the egg and its peeping occupant in his left hand. The motion excited the chick. It tried to raise its head, but its long neck sagged like limp spaghetti until its head rested on Mike's palm.

In this position the chick peeped more loudly than ever. It seemed to sense that a big moment was at hand. With great care Mike worked

on the shell, removing large sections. Using the forceps to push the chick aside, he peered into the bottom of the shell.

"The membranes look good," he remarked, "but there is still quite a bit of yolk. He needs more time." He put the egg back in the incubator and shut the door.

Mike sat down and picked up his book. Feeling a bit better, I sat down, too. Sometimes I watched the chick, sometimes the big clock on the wall.

By five o'clock there had been still more change. Now that half the shell was gone, the chick had been able to get the claws of one foot around the edge of the shell. It seemed to be trying to push itself out. One wing was clear. The head and neck were also totally free. At times the chick would lift its head on the long, frail neck. Then the neck would collapse and the head sink down.

Mike had stopped reading. He sat beside me, watching intently. "One big push might do it," he remarked.

Mike again lifted out the egg. The bird struggled and peeped.

135

Its head wavered and then rested on Mike's palm. Mike was looking into the depths of the shell.

Looking over Mike's shoulder, I could see the glint of moisture and patches of blood at the bottom of the shell. Using the syringe, Mike dribbled in a few drops of water. He explained that it also contained a medicine to shrink the blood vessels and stop any bleeding. He put the egg back in the incubator. Now the chick, looking exhausted, lay half in and half out of the shell. Mike picked up a roll of white sticky tape and made two shoulder straps that held the bird in the shell. The chick looked as though it were wearing overalls.

"There is still too much blood and yolk," Mike explained. "I want to give him more time before he comes out."

It had been a long day. I had spent eight hours in that stuffy room, and I was hungry. But I didn't want to miss anything. "What do you think?" I asked Mike.

"Go ahead and have supper," Mike said. "This little guy isn't going anywhere right now."

136   Two hours later I went back to the incubator room. I found Mike peering into the incubator, and he was smiling. "Look! he said. "He's out and he's okay."

There was the chick, lying on its breast, free at last. The empty shell had been removed. The chick's head nodded in groggy triumph as it tried to get up. The down covering its body was turning from brownish to pinkish yellow as it dried out.

"He just popped out a few minutes ago!" Mike said. "He gave a big push and busted loose. Doesn't he look great!" Mike was beaming with relief and joy.

The chick raised its head, and I heard a tiny, piping whistle. It seemed to say, "I am here! I am a whooping crane, and it's great to be alive!"

Unit Four
Flying

Come Away, Come Away!

J. M. BARRIE

Wendy and her younger brothers, John and Michael, live in a big house in London with their parents, a servant named Liza, and their nursemaid, a Newfoundland dog named Nana.

Peter Pan, a boy who can fly, has come to the children's nursery. Peter likes stories very much, and Wendy has convinced him that she knows a lot of them. Now he is trying to persuade her to come away with him to Neverland, where he lives with some other boys.

"Wendy," said Peter, "do come with me and tell your stories to the other boys."

Of course she was very pleased to be asked, but she said, "Oh, dear, I can't. Think of mummy! Besides, I can't fly."

"I'll teach you."

"Oh, how lovely to fly."

"I'll teach you how to jump on the wind's back, and then away we go."

"Oh!" she exclaimed.

"Wendy, Wendy, when you are sleeping in your silly bed you might be flying about with me saying funny things to the stars."

"Oh!"

"And, Wendy, there are mermaids."

"Mermaids! With tails?"

"Such long tails."

"Oh," cried Wendy, "to see a mermaid!"

He had become frightfully cunning. "Wendy," he said, "how we should all respect you."

She was wriggling her body in distress. It was quite as if she were trying to remain on the nursery floor. But he had no pity for her.

"Wendy," he said, the sly one, "you could tuck us in at night."

"Oh!"

"None of us has ever been tucked in at night."

"Oh," and her arms went out to him.

How could she resist. "Of course, it's awfully fascinating!" she cried. "Peter, would you teach John and Michael to fly too?"

"If you like," he said indifferently. She ran to John and Michael and shook them. "Wake up," she cried, "Peter Pan has come and he is to teach us to fly."

John rubbed his eyes. "Then I shall get up," he said.

Michael was up by this time also, looking as sharp as a knife with six blades. But Peter suddenly signaled for silence. Their faces assumed the craftiness of children listening for sounds from the grown-up world. All was as still as salt. Then everything was right. No, stop! Everything was wrong. Nana, who had been barking distressfully all the evening, was quiet now. It was her silence they had heard.

"Out with the light! Hide! Quick!" cried John, taking command for the only time throughout the whole adventure. And thus when Liza entered, holding Nana, the nursery seemed quite its old self, very dark. And you could have sworn you heard its three wicked inmates breathing angelically as they slept. They were really doing it artfully from behind the window curtains.

Liza was in a bad temper, for she was mixing the Christmas puddings in the kitchen, and had been drawn away from them, with a raisin still on her cheek, by Nana's absurd suspicions. She thought the best way of getting a little quiet was to take Nana to the nursery for a moment, but in custody of course.

"There, you suspicious brute," she said, not sorry that Nana was in disgrace, "they are perfectly safe, aren't they? Every one of the little angels sound asleep in bed. Listen to their gentle breathing."

Here Michael, encouraged by his success, breathed so loudly that they were nearly detected. Nana knew that kind of breathing, and she tried to drag herself out of Liza's clutches.

But Liza was unaware. "No more of it, Nana," she said sternly, pulling her out of the room. "I warn you if you bark again I shall go straight for master and missus and bring them home from the party, and then, oh, won't master whip you, just."

She tied the unhappy dog up again, but do you think Nana ceased to bark? Bring master and missus home from the party! Why, that was just what she wanted. Do you think she cared whether she was whipped so long as her charges were safe? Unfortunately, Liza returned to her puddings, and Nana, seeing that no help would come from her, strained and strained at the chain until at last she broke it. In another moment she had burst into the dining room of Number 27 down the street and flung up her paws to heaven, her most expressive way of making a communication. Mr. and Mrs. Darling knew at once that something terrible was happening in their nursery. Without a good-bye to their hostess they rushed into the street.

But it was now ten minutes since three scoundrels had been breathing behind the curtains, and Peter Pan can do a great deal in ten minutes.

We now return to the nursery.

"It's all right," John announced, emerging from his hiding place. "I say, Peter, can you really fly?"

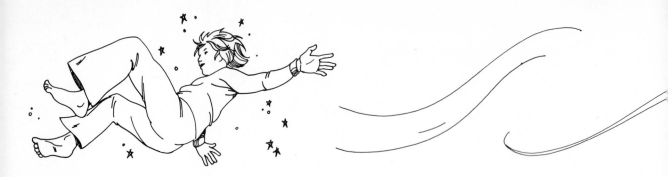

Instead of troubling to answer him, Peter flew around the room, taking the mantelpiece on the way.

"How topping!" said John and Michael.

"How sweet!" cried Wendy.

"Yes, I'm sweet. Oh, I am sweet!" said Peter, forgetting his manners.

It looked delightfully easy, and they tried it first from the floor and then from the bed. But they always went down instead of up.

"I say, how do you do it?" asked John, rubbing his knee. He was quite a practical boy.

"You just think lovely wonderful thoughts," Peter explained, "and they lift you up in the air." He showed them again.

"You're so nippy at it," John said. "Couldn't you do it very slowly once?"

Peter did it both slowly and quickly. "I've got it now, Wendy!" cried John, but soon he found he had not.

Of course, Peter had been trifling with them, for no one can fly unless the fairy dust has been blown on him or her. Fortunately, one of Peter's hands was messy with it, and he blew some on each of them, with the most superb results.

"Now just wriggle your shoulders this way," he said, "and let go."

142

They were all on their beds, and gallant Michael let go
first. He did not quite mean to let go, but he did it, and
immediately he was borne across the room.

"I flewed!" he screamed while still in midair.

John let go and met Wendy near the bathroom.

"Oh, lovely!"

"Oh, ripping!"

"Look at me!"

"Look at me!"

"Look at me!"

They were not nearly so elegant as Peter. They could not
help kicking a little, but their heads were bobbing against
the ceiling, and there is almost nothing so delicious as that.

Up and down they went, and round and round. Heavenly
was Wendy's word.

"I say," cried John, "why shouldn't we all go out?" Of
course, it was to this that Peter had been luring them.

Michael was ready! He wanted to see how long it took
him to do a billion miles. But Wendy hesitated.

"Mermaids!" said Peter again.

"Oh!"

"And there are pirates."

"Pirates," said John, seizing his Sunday hat, "let us go at
once."

It was just at this moment that Mr. and Mrs. Darling hurried with Nana out of Number 27. They ran into the middle of the street to look up at the nursery window. Yes, it was still shut, but the room was ablaze with light. And most heart-gripping sight of all, they could see in shadow on the curtain three little figures in night attire circling round and round, not on the floor but in the air.

Not three figures, four!

In a tremble they opened the street door. Mr. Darling would have rushed upstairs, but Mrs. Darling signaled him to go softly. She even tried to make her heart go softly.

Will they reach the nursery in time? If so, how delightful for them, and we shall all breathe a sigh of relief, but there will be no story. On the other hand, if they are not in time, I solemnly promise that it will all come right in the end.

They would have reached the nursery in time had it not been that the little stars were watching them. Once again the stars blew the window open, and that smallest star of all called out, "To Neverland, Peter!"

Then Peter knew that there was not a moment to lose. "Come," he cried imperiously, and soared out at once into the night, followed by John and Michael and Wendy.

Mr. and Mrs. Darling and Nana rushed into the nursery too late. The birds were flown.

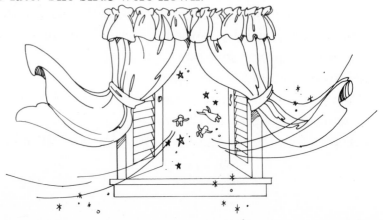

Leonardo's Strange Dream

ELIZABETH L. CRANDALL

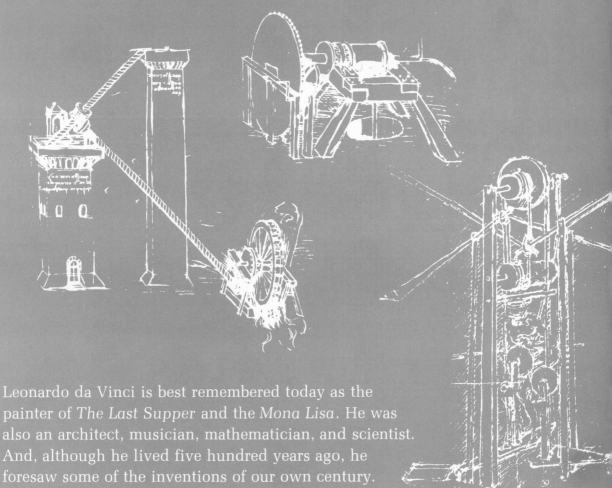

Leonardo da Vinci is best remembered today as the painter of *The Last Supper* and the *Mona Lisa*. He was also an architect, musician, mathematician, and scientist. And, although he lived five hundred years ago, he foresaw some of the inventions of our own century.

Leonardo liked anything that was mechanical. He drew designs for a machine for digging earth, and for a bridge that would swing sideways when drawn open by a pulley and chain. He also designed many other things to save time and labor.

145

One of Leonardo's inventions was a cart that was moved by springs. He realized that when a cart turns a corner, a wheel on the outside of the curve has to travel over a greater distance than an inside wheel. He designed what we would call a differential gear, so that the wheels of his cart could revolve at different rates of speed.

The invention Leonardo wanted most to make was a flying machine. Other men before him had believed artificial wings could be made that would beat the air like the wings of a bird. Their ideas had not been taken very seriously by people who had never heard of an automobile, a train, or a steamboat, much less of an airplane. People rode on horses, in carriages, in boats that were moved by oars or sails, or else they walked.

Leonardo had never forgotten a strange dream he had when he freed some birds from their cages and watched them fly. He believed that some day people would be able to travel through the air, too. When he lived in Milan, he had designed several models of flying machines. He had also invented a parachute. Leonardo had a great deal of self-confidence. But he did seem to realize that a parachute might come in handy if he ever took to the air in one of his machines!

One of Leonardo's designs for a flying machine showed a board to which wings were attached. A person was to lie face down on the board and work the wings by moving his or her arms and legs.

None of Leonardo's first designs was practical. They would not work because there was no form of power strong enough to get the machine off the ground and keep it in the air. Manpower was not enough.

"Perhaps it would be better to make a machine that

does not need power," Leonardo decided after much thought. "Perhaps it would be better to use only air currents to keep the machine in the air."

He studied the way a bird's wings act when going in the same direction as the air currents, and how they act when going against the wind. He filled page after page in his notebooks with pictures and descriptions.

At last he built a machine which he called the "Great Bird." The machine was really a glider. He thought that it should take off from a high place, such as a cliff. Then air currents would keep it in the air.

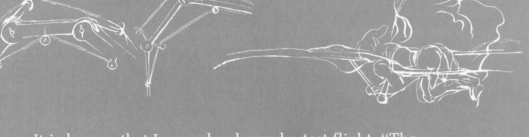

It is known that Leonardo planned a test flight. "The Great Bird," he wrote in his notebook, "will fill the world with amazement." But the notebooks do not say whether the test was actually made. It probably was, and it probably failed. If the test had been successful, the world would have been filled with amazement, just as Leonardo said. Italy and all of Europe would have been talking about Leonardo the flier.

Leonardo must have been very much disappointed. He had hoped to be the first person to make a successful flight. He was still sure that his strange dream would come true. Someday—maybe it would be many years in the future—people *would* learn to fly.

How Birds Fly

RUSSELL FREEDMAN

The flapping flight of birds is not fully understood even today. Birds and airplanes are subject to the same laws of aerodynamics. Yet the rigid wing of a plane is simple indeed compared with the flapping wing of a bird. So many different forces act upon a beating wing that it may never be possible to understand them all. However, many principles of flapping flight have been discovered, mainly through high-speed photography.

In order to be lifted by its wings, a bird or plane must be moving forward fast enough to make air rush past the wings. A plane is driven through the air by its propellers. As the propellers push air backward, the plane shoots forward. The faster the air is pushed back, the faster the plane moves ahead. A jet plane moves forward by pushing hot gases backward.

A bird moves forward by flapping its wings. As the wings beat up and down, the inner wing does not move much. This part of the wing works just like the outstretched wing of a plane. It supplies the lift that holds the bird up. Most of the flapping is done by the outer wing, where primary flight feathers beat against the air. These flight feathers work like a plane's propellers. They push air backward, driving the bird forward.

A bird's flight feathers overlap each other. When the bird pulls its wings down, the flight feathers snap shut, like slats closing in a Venetian blind. Now the wings are almost airtight. They can push with great force against the air.

The downstroke is the power stroke. With each downward wing beat, the bird drives itself forward. As the tightly closed wing comes down, the inner wing moves only a little. The outer wing sweeps forward and downward toward the bird's head. The primary flight feathers bite into the air like small propellers. Each flight feather twists sharply and pushes backward against the air as a propeller does.

When the bird pulls its wings up, the flight feathers snap open, like slats opening in a Venetian blind. With the feathers spread apart, air passes easily through the wings. This makes it easier for the bird to raise its wings.

The upstroke does not provide much forward power. A bird pulls its wings up mainly to get them back into place for the next downstroke. Now the wings sweep upward and backward, away from the bird's head. The flight feathers still push against the air, but not as strongly as before. By the end of the upstroke, the bird's body has pulled ahead of its wings. An instant later the wings start moving forward and downward again.

By looking at the size and shape of a bird's wings, you can often tell how the bird lives. Short, rounded wings are a clue that the bird lives in woods, shrubs, or underbrush. Small songbirds that perch on branches have short, rounded wings. They can dart and twist through trees and bushes without hurting themselves. Stubby wings are also found among many birds of the forest and among ground-feeding birds like woodcocks and quail. These birds can turn sharply in tight places. They can make quick escapes by flapping hard and fast for short distances, but they cannot fly fast for very long.

Long, pointed wings mean that the bird lives in open country or near the sea. These birds are fast fliers. They sweep through the sky, often snatching their food out of the air. High-speed wings are found among land birds like falcons, swallows, and swifts, among shore birds like sandpipers and plovers, and among most birds that migrate long distances.

The biggest wings belong to birds that glide and soar much of the time. Sea soarers like gulls, shearwaters, and albatrosses have very long, narrow wings with sharp tips. They sail along with the winds. Land soarers like eagles, hawks, and vultures have very wide wings with deep slots in the wing tips. The slots prevent stalling as the birds circle slowly overhead.

You can always tell how big or small a bird is by the speed of its wing beats. Since small wings have less lifting power than big ones, small birds must flap quickly, while large birds can flap more slowly. A vulture beats its giant wings about once a second. Each stroke drives the vulture forward with great force. Medium-sized birds like ducks and crows flap 2 or 3 times a second. A sparrow beats its stubby wings about 14 times a second, while the smaller chickadee flaps 25 times a second. Of all birds, humming-

151

birds are the smallest. A ruby-throated hummingbird beats its tiny wings about 70 times a second. Hummingbirds get their name from the humming sound made by their rapidly beating wings.

A hummingbird's wings work differently from those of other birds. The wings are shaped like stiff paddles. They move only at the shoulders, where they swivel freely in almost any direction. This makes it possible for a hummingbird to hover, or "stand still," in the air as it sips nectar from a flower. While hovering, it keeps its body upright. As its wings sweep forward, they twist sharply toward the ground and push air downward. As the wings sweep back, they flip over. Now the top of each wing faces the ground and again pushes air downward. The wings act like the whirling rotor of a helicopter, which also drives air downward. Besides hanging motionless in the air, a hummingbird can fly straight up and even backward, which no other bird can do.

A bird's flying speed depends partly on where the bird is going. A sparrow cruises along at 15 or 20 miles an hour. When it heads home to roost, it may speed up to 25 miles an hour. If it is chased by an enemy, it can fly 35 miles an hour. Its speed is also affected by the wind. When the bird flies with the wind at its tail, it gets an extra push from behind. If it turns around and heads into the wind, the bird passes more slowly over the ground.

Flight speed depends mainly on the design of a bird's wings. Songbirds with short, rounded wings normally fly between 15 and 25 miles an hour. Swallows and starlings use their long, pointed wings to fly 40 or 50 miles an hour. Ducks and geese reach speeds of 60 miles an hour or more. The fastest birds are probably falcons and swifts, whose wings sweep back like those of a jet. A peregrine falcon, or duck hawk, can approach 100 miles an hour. The speed record for level flight is held by an Indian swift, which was clocked at the amazing speed of 200 miles an hour.

We humans have watched birds fly for thousands of years. Until recent times we knew little about what happens when a bird speeds through the air. High-speed photography gave us our first close-up look, revealing birds in flight as they had never been seen before.

Today we are studying flying birds with the aid of motion pictures, wind tunnels, electronic computers, and mathematical formulas. The flapping wings of a bird, with their millions of twisting and bending parts, are far more complicated than the rigid wings of any aircraft. We know more about bird flight than our ancestors even suspected. But we still don't understand everything that happens when a bird beats its wings and takes to the sky.

The Horse That Flew

ZENA SUTHERLAND

Once, in the early days when the gods and goddesses of Greece had magic powers, there was a terrible monster called the Chimera. It had three heads. One was the head of a goat, one was the head of a lion, and the third was the head of a snake. Breathing smoke and fire, it had laid waste the lands of Caria and Lycia. Its flames scorched the earth and killed the people who came near it. The king of Lycia promised Bellerophon a reward if he killed the Chimera. Bellerophon and the king's daughter loved one another and hoped that as a reward, her father would let them get married. Bellerophon was a brave young man. Although he loved the princess, he feared the monster. Therefore, he decided to seek advice before beginning his task.

"No man can go near the Chimera and live," a wise old man told Bellerophon, "for it breathes flames. Only if you take it by surprise can you destroy the monster. To do so, you must be able to attack it from the air. For this you will need the flying horse, Pegasus. First you must find him, and then you must tame him." So Bellerophon went to the faraway mountain where, it was said, the magic horse came to drink the pure water of the mountain stream.

Bellerophon watched and waited for many days, and he wondered how it would be possible to tame a wild, winged horse. One night he dreamed that the goddess Athena gave him a golden bridle that would tame Pegasus. The goddess saw his dream and wanted to help Bellerophon. When he woke from his sleep, there indeed was a golden bridle lying beside him! As he picked up the bridle, he saw the beautiful horse floating down from the sky, its silvery wings outspread.

Holding the golden bridle, Bellerophon sprang to the horse's back, and the startled animal flew high into the sky. Then, trying to unseat the rider, Pegasus dropped to earth like a stone. But Bellerophon held on. He slipped the golden bridle over the wild creature's head, and at once Pegasus was tamed.

After he had flown on Pegasus for some days, Bellerophon knew his steed's power. He felt that, with such help, he could destroy the Chimera and escape. He buckled on his sword, grasped his shield, and mounted the horse. Together they flew toward Lycia, where the monster hid in its cave. When Bellerophon saw below him a broad path of burned, black earth, he knew the Chimera was nearby.

155

Three spirals of smoke rose into the air. They must be from the three heads of the monster, Bellerophon decided, and he gave his horse the signal to descend. There was the Chimera, lurking in its cave. Its three heads were more terrible than anything he had ever imagined. Still, when Pegasus swooped down, Bellerophon quickly cut off the goat's head and was carried safely back into the sky. When he made his next attack, he was not as lucky. He did wound the lion's head, but he could not destroy it.

On his third attack, Bellerophon was almost overcome by the flames and Pegasus was terrified, for the Chimera

threw itself upward in a rage and clung to the horse's flanks. Horse and rider were in danger of being eaten by the flames. But then Bellerophon drove his sword into the beast's neck and the Chimera fell to earth, hissing and roaring. There it died, burned by its own fire.

Bellerophon and Pegasus flew back to the mountain where they drank the healing waters and rested. Although he had done the task set by the king, Bellerophon had to perform other tasks before the king would let his daughter marry the young hero. Through all of these trials, the flying horse was a faithful and loving companion.

Something Told the Wild Geese

Something told the wild geese
 It was time to go.
Though the fields lay golden
 Something whispered, "Snow."
Leaves were green and stirring,
 Berries, luster-glossed,
But beneath warm feathers
 Something cautioned, "Frost."

All the sagging orchards
 Steamed with amber spice,
But each wild breast stiffened
 At remembered ice.
Something told the wild geese
 It was time to fly—
Summer sun was on their wings,
 Winter in their cry.

—Rachel Field

Sumi's Prize

YOSHIKO UCHIDA

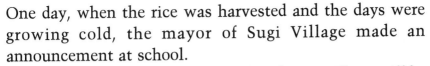

One day, when the rice was harvested and the days were growing cold, the mayor of Sugi Village made an announcement at school.

"Harrumph," he said, clearing his throat. "There will be a kite flying contest on the banks of the river on New Year's Day. There will be a prize for the best and most beautiful kite." Then he tapped his head as though his top hat were sitting on it and added, "I shall be the judge."

Sumi's hand flew up. "Can girls enter?" she asked.

"Why not?" the mayor said. "The contest is open to all the children of the village."

At last, a chance to win a prize! Sumi was very good at folding paper cranes and flowers. She was sure she could make a good kite with a little help from Father. She would make the most beautiful kite in all the village and she would win the prize. The more she thought of it, the more Sumi felt she could win.

There was one problem, however, and that was her brother Taro. He would enter the contest too and if Father helped him as well, his kite would be better, for they had made many beautiful kites together. Sumi was worried, but that night Taro gave her a nice surprise.

159

"I'm making my kite alone," he announced.

So Sumi began to work on her kite. First she drew the design on a piece of paper. The kite would be in the shape of a great butterfly and she would paint it gold and black. She went to the stationers to buy string and paint and the proper kind of paper. Sumi worked hard for many days and when she was ready, Mother cooked some starch to make the paste.

Then Father helped her put the kite together.

"The kite must be light and it must be strong," Father said. "And it must be properly balanced."

Sumi made three kites before she finally made one that was just right. Then Father went with her to the river's edge to try it out. On the very first try, Sumi's golden butterfly soared into the sky as though that was where it belonged. Sumi watched it happily and shouted, "I'm going to win the prize!"

But when Taro finished his kite, she was not so sure. His kite was sturdy and bold with the face of a *samurai* warrior glaring from it in purple, red and yellow. It looked fierce enough to batter down Sumi's butterfly.

If only both of us could win, Sumi thought. But she knew very well there was only one prize.

Now that her kite was ready, Sumi could scarcely wait for New Year's Day. She waited and she worried as the first snows came and left the ground laced with patches of white. But when New Year's Day came at last, the weather was bright and clear and exactly right for flying kites.

161

Sumi put on her new silk kimono. "Happy New Year!" she called. "Today is the day of the contest!"

"Well, well, so it is," Father said, as though he had forgotten.

Mother had prepared all sorts of wonderful things for their special New Year's breakfast.

After breakfast they went to the shrine to ask for the blessings of a good year. Sumi said her prayers as fast as she could and ran home ahead of the others. She took off her kimono, folded it carefully and put it away. Kimonos were all right for saying New Year prayers but not for flying kites.

Sumi hurried into her warm slacks and her big wooly sweater. She took the red bows from her hair and tied her braids back so they would not flop in her face. She put new laces in her sneakers so she would not trip as she ran with her kite. She inspected her kite over and over again to make sure it had not come loose anywhere. Then she was ready.

After lunch they all started for the river bank where the contest would be held. Taro ran ahead to look at the kites his friends had made.

Sumi walked with Father. She held her golden butterfly in one hand. The closer they got to the river, the more her feet seemed to want to turn around and go home. She looked up at Father, but he seemed eager to reach the river bank. "The wind is just right," he said.

There were already many people at the river's edge when they arrived, and Sumi saw the girls in her class. Not one was wearing slacks and sneakers. Not one was holding a kite. Sumi swallowed hard. She was the only girl in the whole village to enter the contest.

Sumi saw the mayor in his black frock coat, his striped trousers, and his shiny top hat. She had not seen him look so elegant since the day he was elected mayor. He stood at a table draped with red and white bunting and bowed as he wished everyone a happy new year.

Now the boys lined up in front of him with their kites, and Mother urged Sumi along.

"Good luck!" she whispered.

Sumi found a place at the end of the line and looked anxiously at the other kites. There were all kinds of kites, and they were all sizes and shapes. One was square and another was diamond-shaped. One was a hollowed-out box and another was a snowman. Some were decorated with many colors and some were painted with dragons, for this was the first day of the Year of the Dragon. No one had a warrior as fierce as Taro's. And no one had a golden butterfly. Sumi thought hers was the most beautiful kite of them all.

The mayor walked up and down inspecting the kites. "Very fine," he murmured. "Very fine."

He paused for a moment in front of Sumi and nodded. "Ah," he said, but that was all.

Sumi wanted to tell him how hard she had worked on her kite, but her tongue wouldn't move. She wanted to wish him a happy new year, but all she could do was scratch the tip of her nose.

Then it was time to get the kites up. Father helped Sumi get her butterfly into the air and then it was all up to her. Carefully, carefully, she let out the string, tugging to keep her butterfly climbing higher and higher.

"Climb! Climb!" Sumi shouted to her butterfly.

It seemed to hear her, for it soared up and up, straight toward the sun. From the corner of her eye, Sumi could see Taro's warrior. It was soaring too, but her butterfly was

163

going higher. It truly was. Sumi knew that she would win, for if she could beat Taro, she knew she could beat anybody. Now, at last, she would have her prize!

Sumi glanced at the mayor to be sure that he saw her kite. He was watching it with his head tipped back, shading his eyes from the sun. And then it happened! A gust of wind swooped along the bank of the river and swept his top hat right off his head. It went whirling along the sand straight toward the water.

"My hat!" the mayor shouted. "My hat!"

"Stop!" Sumi shouted. But the hat was such a nice round shape for rolling, it just whirled on and on.

"The mayor's hat!" Sumi called out. But everyone was too busy looking up to notice what was going on below.

It was hard to watch her kite and the hat as well, but Sumi knew she must help the mayor. Now the hat was at the water's edge and Sumi had to save it. She took one last look at her golden butterfly and then, holding tight to its string, she ran as fast as she could. She threw herself on the hat with a great thud and felt it flatten beneath her. She had saved the hat, but she had squashed it flat. Worse still, she had given her kite such a jerk that it turned upside down and came tumbling from the sky. Like a wounded bird, her golden butterfly zigzagged to earth and crumpled in a heap on the sand.

"Ohhhhh." A sad cry rippled through the crowd like a winter wind, for now everyone saw what had happened.

The mayor ran to Sumi's side. "Are you all right, little one?" he asked, and he helped her to her feet.

Sumi nodded. "My kite's broken," she said sadly, "and I squashed your hat."

The mayor looked sad too. "I am sorry about your kite,"

he said. "It was a fine kite. But don't worry about my hat."
He knew a few things about top hats that Sumi didn't know.

"Watch," he said, and he whacked the hat on his arm. It
popped up with a zing, looking as though it had never been
under Sumi's stomach at all. The mayor put the hat back on
his head and took Sumi's hand.

"Come with me," he said, and he led her to the judging
table with the red and white bunting.

Mother and Father hurried to Sumi's side. "Are you all
right?" they asked. "We saw you save the mayor's hat!" they
added proudly.

The mayor let Sumi sit beside him at the table, and like
two solemn judges they watched the bright kites speckle the
holiday sky.

Sumi saw Taro's warrior soaring above all the others and
she knew he would win. Now he would have the prize while
she still had none. Sumi wanted to cry. She had come so
close to winning.

165

Soon it was time to pull down the kites and the mayor asked everyone to gather around. The prize was a beautiful box of watercolor paints and everyone clapped when it went to Taro, for his kite had truly flown best of all. The contest was over and people began to drift away.

The mayor, however, was not finished. "Just a moment," he said, and he fumbled about in his pockets. Finally he pulled out his big blue fountain pen.

"I seem to have another prize," he said. "It is for the only person in Sugi Village to rescue a top hat from the river!"

Then the mayor, wearing his beautiful top hat, shook Sumi's hand and gave her his own fountain pen. Sumi was sure she must be dreaming. Everyone clapped and cheered. They were glad there was another prize for Sumi. The girls from her class crowded about her wanting to take turns holding the pen in their hands.

"The mayor's own pen!" they said in excited voices. "That's the best prize there ever was."

166

Let's Make a Kite

JACK STOKES

When you see a kite floating way up in the sky, do you wish that you had one too?

You can make your own kite, something that flies and is yours. It can look very special and it's fun to do.

First you need two long lightweight sticks. Use strips from old window shades, bamboo blinds, or wooden moldings. Or buy carpenter's dowels about as thick as a pencil.

The up-and-down stick is called a spine. You can cut it 75 centimeters long for this kite. The cross stick is called a spar. Make it 60 centimeters long. Cut a slit in both ends of each stick, or make notches with a file.

Make a mark 20 centimeters from the top of the spine. Measure 30 centimeters from either end of the spar and mark that too. Cross the spine and the spar on these marks. Then tie and glue the sticks together.

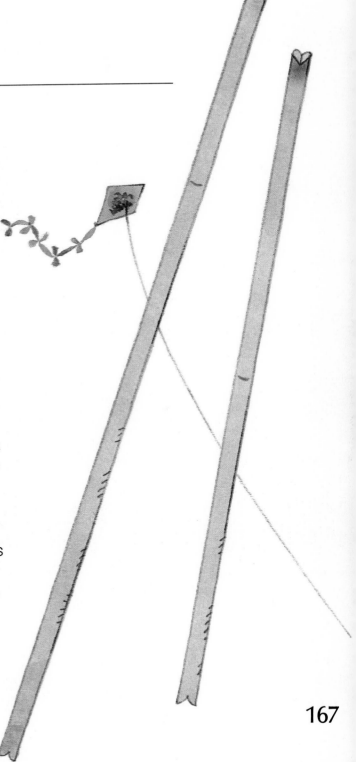

167

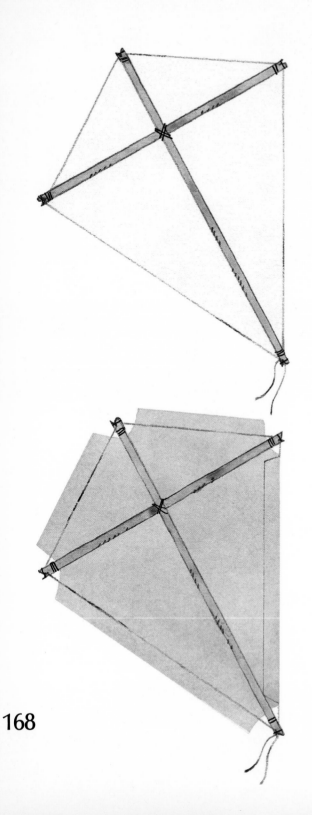

After the glue dries, run a string snugly around the notches. This makes a frame for the paper covering. Tie and knot both ends of the string at the bottom. Leave several centimeters hanging down to attach a tail when it is ready.

With some strong thread, wrap a few turns at the bottom of each notch. This will prevent the wood from splitting. Then make a few more turns at the end of each stick and knot tightly. This will keep the string from slipping loose. Sticky tape may be used in place of thread.

To cover your kite, use newsprint, brown mailing paper, gift wrapping, or crepe paper. It should be larger than the kite frame. You can tape two pieces together.

Have someone hold the frame on the back of your paper. Draw an outline around the string shape. Remove the kite and cut the covering about 2 centimeters larger than this outline. Snip off the corners of the paper. With the spine facing down, fold the paper over the string. Glue it down neatly and let it dry. You may use see-through tape instead of glue if you press it down firmly.

168

From the back of your kite punch two small holes with a pencil. Later you will run a flying line through these holes to tie it to the frame. Use gummed reinforcements or tape around the holes to keep them from tearing. To be extra safe, put the reinforcements or tape on both the front and back of the kite.

Now you can paint the front of your kite just the way you want to. Draw airplanes, faces, ships, birds, fish, your initials, or anything you like. Make it big and bright so your kite will show up when it's flying high overhead.

Next you need a ball of strong lightweight string for the flying line. From the front, run the string through one hole, around the crossed sticks, and then out the other hole. Knot the string securely.

To make a tail, use old cotton sheets, curtains, dresses, or shirts. Cut or tear long strips 5 centimeters wide. Tie them together until the tail is 4 meters long. Cut the rest of your strips into pieces 30 centimeters long. Use lots of colors if you like. Tie one of these pieces in a bow about every 30 centimeters on the tail. Use a double knot. When you are finished, attach this tail to the piece of string you left hanging at the bottom of your kite.

169

It's time to fly your kite! Pick a sunny day when there are no storm clouds. The breeze should be steady. The best place is a beach, a park, or a huge open area without any buildings, trees, or wires to get in your way.

Stand with your back to the wind. Get a friend to stand away from you, holding the kite with the paper side toward the wind and the tail stretched out straight. When the breeze pushes on the kite, your helper can toss it up. Let the string out as fast as your kite will take it. Sometimes running into the wind helps too. You will soon get the feel of the gentle pull on the string when everything is right.

It's a wonderful feeling to watch a kite that you made sail up in the air. With a little luck it will stay there. Wind in the string when you want to bring the kite down. Then you are ready to fly it again and again and again . . .

Night Plane

The midnight plane with its riding lights
looks like a footloose star
wandering west through the blue-black night
to where the mountains are,

a star that's journeyed nearer earth
to tell each quiet farm
and little town, "Put out your lights,
children of earth. Sleep warm."

—Frances M. Frost

Flight

The doctor said, Count to ten.
One (a funny mask on my face),
two (I knew the doctor was kind but)
three, they promised ice—, four,
I can't, five, say five,

                    and I

was flying up over the roof
with crowds of red and blue balloons
like the time I sneaked up in the air
with my uncle in his scalawag plane
and looked below to the ribbon rivers
and fields of puzzles fitted together—

and I still have never told my mother
that I flew that day, that I flew away,
a plane
        a kite
                a balloon
                    a child
beyond her worried hands.

—Ruth Whitman

Ondine

M. M. OSBORNE, JR.

Ondine is a young sandpiper who is fascinated by the stars. The Big Dipper is her particular favorite. She even tries to fly to this constellation instead of migrating south with the other sandpipers. Then she receives some good advice from a wise old owl.

Ondine, like all migrating birds, had a voice built into her, almost like an alarm clock, that said about mid-November, "It is time! Fly south!" This alarm clock would speak to her each fall as long as she lived, just as it would tell her in the spring, "Now! It is time to go northward again!"

The other sandpipers had long since heard the mid-November voice and were well on their way to Florida and the warm Gulf waters. So far Ondine had not heard the call. It had sounded once or twice during her flight up the coast, but so intent had she been to reach the stars that she had not heard.

Now, in the chill evening on the Greenland shore, as she and the old owl gazed up at the southbound geese, the old instinct fairly shouted inside her, so strong that it almost frightened her.

"South?" she asked. "South? But where?" And she wondered if the South was like the place where the stars come up, like the Dipper—calling you endlessly, but never to be found.

173

The owl seemed to read her mind. "Oh, you'll find it," he said cheerfully. "*All* sandpipers do." Then he added firmly, "But you'll need some sleep; I wouldn't start until morning if I were you. Just behind this stump is a comfortable place, and you may rest there for tonight."

"But——" Ondine started.

"No buts, if you please! Off to sleep and straight for the Southland tomorrow," said Old Nick. "Perhaps another year you and I may search together for the northern stars."

Ondine dutifully crept around behind the stump, where a bit of a broken branch projected a few inches over the sand, forming a little shelter. She nested in and, as she had not done in a long time, covered her feet with sand. She settled down, and the stars came out and blazed in the northern sky. Ondine watched the Dipper rise, and then, as she had done on the shore so long ago, blew a kiss at it and said softly, "Goodbye!"

The next day Ondine began her journey. She flew steadily south along the coast and then, obeying some instinct, turned southwesterly. Until she left the shoreline, she camped every night on a beach and caught some fish or seaworms to eat. After turning inland she flew almost steadily night and day, feeling neither tired nor hungry. Once she stopped on the shore of a lake where hundreds of ducks were sheltered for the night. But the ducks made so much noise that after that she landed only when absolutely necessary. She began to hope that she might meet some other sandpipers, but they had all gone south weeks before, and she saw not a one.

175

One day, over Kansas, she had a close call with a hawk. She was flying quite low and looking down at the flat brown-yellow plains. Suddenly she saw the shadow of a large bird rapidly drawing closer to her small shadow. Without knowing why, she veered sharply to the left. She was thoroughly surprised and scared to see a big red-shouldered hawk, with talons spread, plummet right through the place where she had just been. With a shrill cry of rage and disappointment the hawk turned sharply up from his dive and began to come at Ondine again. Now she realized that the hawk intended to kill her if he could, and she took desperate flight.

Sandpipers are fast and tricky fliers, being able to turn almost at right angles to their course of flight in an instant. Ondine dodged and twisted at top speed, while the hawk narrowly missed her in several passes. Though much faster on the straightaway than Ondine, he could not match her rapid turns. After almost an hour she spied a clump of trees near a farmhouse and slipped in among the sheltering branches just as the hawk pulled up, screeching with frustration, from a final dive. She sat exhausted and panting on a branch well covered with leaves, hanging on with trembling feet.

"Well!" said a small friendly voice. "You certainly gave *him* a chase! I never saw such flying!"

Ondine was startled, but in looking around saw just above her a brown bird with a spotted white breast and a reddish brown tail. His eye was bright and cheerful, and he seemed to be looking at her with a lively concern. She felt instantly reassured and very happy to have some companionship.

Still panting, she said, "What *was* that thing? I've never had anything like that happen before!"

"*That*, my friend, was the local bully—a hawk known in these parts as the Slasher, and a good name it is for him, the beast! You did well to get away in one piece."

"Is he like that to everyone?" asked Ondine, beginning to get her breath.

"Oh no!" laughed the other. "Just to small, catchable travelers like you and me. I understand he doesn't dare make a pass at anything larger than a robin. I came in at night, and he didn't see me—some friends of mine had warned me—and I'm waiting for the dark to fall again before I go on."

"Oh," said Ondine, "don't you live here?"

"My gracious, no. I spend my summers in the Adirondacks, and am just traveling through to the Gulf Coast. How about you?"

177

Ondine explained that she had grown up on the Massachusetts shore, and that now she was on her way south.

"I don't know where to go, really," she said, half apologizing. "My—my family went on before me." Then she asked, "Do you know my family—the Sandpipers?"

The other bird, pretending to think about it, said, "Sandpiper—Sandpiper—mm, not related to the Plovers, by any chance?"

Ondine had never met any plovers and said honestly, "No, I don't think so. Who is your family?"

The other bird, hesitating a moment, said, "At the moment I am traveling alone. My family is wintering in South Carolina. Thrush is my name—Hermit Thrush."

"How do you do?" said Ondine politely. "My name is Ondine."

"Delighted to meet you," returned the thrush. Then in a more practical tone, he asked, "Now, just where is it you are staying for the winter?"

"I don't really know," said Ondine, and then, unable to confess that she had never been south before, she added, "I haven't really thought about it. I'm looking for a quiet place near the shore—I'm a shorebird, you know—some place not absolutely cluttered up with terns."

The thrush mused for a minute, then said, "Don't care much for the shore, myself, but I have stayed overnight near a little beach on the Gulf Coast and found it charming. Nice little clump of hardwood trees nearby." He cleared his throat delicately and said, glancing at Ondine, "As a matter of fact, I'd kind of toyed with the idea of going there this winter."

"Oh!" cried Ondine joyfully. "Do you think you could show me the way?"

"Be delighted," said the thrush, a little stiffly but still looking pleased. "I think we'd better wait until dark."

"Oh, yes—because of Slasher!" interrupted Ondine, who had nearly forgotten about her narrow escape.

"That's right," said the thrush. "And now, I think I'll take a little nap before we start."

They slept quietly, although Ondine, not being a tree-dwelling bird, found it hard at first to hang on and sleep. When darkness had fully descended, the thrush woke her and whispered, "All right? It's time!"

They slipped quietly through the trees and, after looking out to make sure the coast was clear, flew noiselessly off, close to the ground.

For some time they pushed on. Then suddenly Ondine saw flashes of lightning far ahead.

"Looks like a storm up ahead," said the thrush. "I think we should look for some shelter soon."

Soon the wind began to pick up, and Ondine could feel an occasional drop of rain. It felt cool and good after the lifeless hot air they had been in.

Suddenly the air began to rush at them, and they heard a roaring noise coming closer and closer. The thrush yelled, "Get to ground quick! It's a twister!"

Before Ondine could ask what a twister might be, she felt herself taken up by the wind, as if in a giant hand, and hurled skyward.

"Mr. Thrush! Mr. Thrush!" she shouted, trying to look around. But she neither saw him nor heard him. The roar of the wind drowned out everything, and the darkness was

179

intense. She tried to fly, but was sent tumbling over and over in the sky, not sure of which was up or down. Little hailstones pelted her body, and one, hitting her hard on the beak, nearly knocked her out. She struggled to keep some kind of balance, but the wind was too strong. She kept calling out for the thrush, but the wind tore the words from her bill. She could not even hear herself.

The twister raced on over the plain and covered more than 300 miles before it died out. Inside it Ondine fought to keep upright—fought as she never had before, choking and spluttering with the dust. Her long flight stood her in good stead. She was as tough and strong as a sandpiper can be, and possibly she owed her life to this. She was also lucky. Rocks and bits of wood picked up by the tornado whizzed by without once touching her, although any one of them could have killed her. She passed out from exhaustion a few times, but coming to again struck out the best she could in an effort to get out of the storm.

About four o'clock the twister began to lose force, and Ondine dimly realized that she could fly for a few seconds against the wall of wind. Then, as suddenly as it had begun, the roaring ceased. Ondine, no longer supported by the wind, literally fell out of the storm. Still in a daze, she flew aimlessly about, aware of nothing but a dull, throbbing pain where the hailstone had struck her bill.

Miraculously, she turned in the right direction and saw it—she was sure of it! It was the Big Dipper—brighter, and bigger, and closer than it had ever been before—right ahead!

She summoned the last of her strength and flew straight for it, sure in her heart that all would be well.

Inside the Big Dipper Diner (Bill Rogers, Prop.) two truck drivers in checked shirts and denim pants were sitting at the counter eating pancakes and drinking coffee.

"You guys see anything of that twister they had north of here?" Rogers asked.

"No sir!" said one of the drivers. "We were coming in from the other side, and it wasn't near us."

181

Bill yawned and then glanced out through the window. It was nearly five o'clock, and the sky was beginning to lighten with the dawn. "Gotta turn out the sign," he said, coming around the counter and making for the door. "Getting too light out to keep it on."

Bill was especially proud of his diner's electric sign. It had cost him a lot. It certainly had helped his night and early morning business, though. The truckers could see it for miles, and most of them liked to travel in the cool of the nighttime.

Now, as he did every morning, he stepped outside onto the highway to have a last look at his neon sign before turning it off. There it was—a big electric dipper in yellow, with extra bunches of tubing at the corners, where the stars should be, to make it extra real. He smiled with satisfaction and then started back inside to turn it off.

As he approached the door, a small speckled brown object caught his eye, lying in the corner of the doorway. He stooped over and saw that it was a bird. At first he thought it was dead, but on closer inspection he could see it breathing ever so slightly. Quickly he bent down and cupped it in his hand, finding it still warm and alive, although unconscious. Very excited, he pushed into the diner, with the bird nestled in his hand.

"Look at this! Just look!" said Bill, showing the bird to the truckers. "Why, it's a sandpiper! I haven't seen one of them since I was a boy back in Maine!"

"Alive?" asked a trucker.

"Yes, it's alive," said Bill softly, peering intently at the bird and feeling it gently with his finger. "Doesn't seem to have broken anything—more like it's all tuckered out."

"Do you suppose it could have got blown here in that twister?" asked the other trucker.

"Yeah! I'll bet that's it, all right."

The three—Bill on his side of the counter, the drivers leaning over toward him from theirs—were huddled around the bird in the old man's hand.

"Pretty little thing, ain't it. Look! You can see its heart beating!" said the big driver softly.

"What kind d'you say it was?" asked the other.

"A sandpiper," said Bill. "They're all over the beaches back in New England."

"Here, Bill," broke in the big driver, "reach me that cup there." He took it, looked around for a minute, and then said, "Got some tissue? Fine!" He took the soft tissue and very deliberately tore it into shreds, packing them carefully in the cup until it was about half full. "Now Bill, lay it in there. It'll be warm and comfy."

Very gently, Bill transferred the bird to the nest in the cup, where it lay quietly. He took another tissue and, after soaking it in cold water, wadded it up and held it very gently against the bird's forehead, just over the bill. The three leaned closer. The bird's eyes fluttered and opened.

"A-a-h!" said Bill, "I think she'll be okay!" The truckers were smiling broadly.

When Ondine awoke she felt she must be dreaming. She smelled a heavenly smell of hot dogs and coffee. It was dry and warm and soft where she lay, and she could hear the sound of people talking. Her bill ached where the hailstone had struck it. But then something cool and pleasantly moist was applied to the sore part, and the pain disappeared. She

183

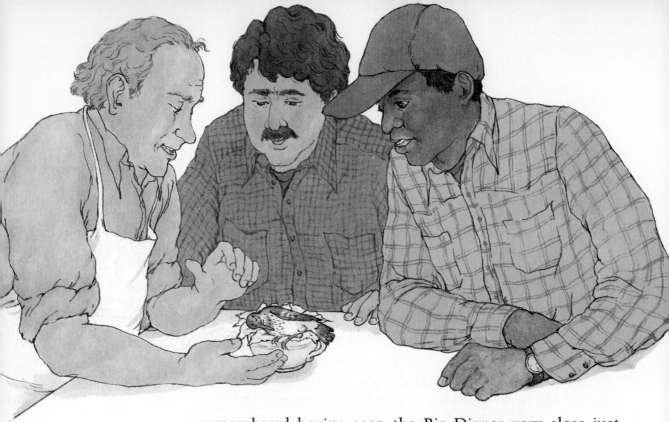

remembered having seen the Big Dipper very close just before she had passed out, and suddenly she felt that she had reached the stars!

She opened her eyes. What she saw was three kindly brown faces all peering at her, and around them a snug little room, rough finished but clean and white. Presently, a bottle cap filled with cool water was placed near her bill, and leaning out slightly from the cup in which she lay, she drank the water.

"A-a-h!" sighed the three men. "Just look at that!"

She slept awhile. When she again woke up, it was full daylight. Two of the men had gone, but the oldest remained, quietly gazing at her. She stirred, and he offered her another bottle cap full of water, which she drank eagerly. Feeling much better, she stood up and hopped off the edge of the cup to the counter. A few potato chips lay around, and Ondine ate part of one. Finding she was tired, she returned to the nest in the cup and slept long and comfortably.

Much later, when she woke up, it was dark again. She looked around, but the old man was not to be seen. She was frightened at first, but then she heard him snoring in the back room. She felt deliciously cozy and peaceful, and quite awake. She began to think back over the events of the day before.

She remembered getting caught up in a terrible wind and, before that, starting off to find a place on the shore with—who was it? Yes!—Mr. Thrush. She wondered what had happened to him, poor bird. Had he made it through the storm? She had a pang of grief at the thought of his perhaps being dead. She vowed to herself that she would seek him out as soon as her strength came back.

Then she looked around again and decided that, whatever else she might do, this place, full of warmth and kindness and good food—this place marked by the Big Dipper—would be her winter home.

And so it became. She soon recovered her strength and ate more of what Old Bill set out for her. He was endlessly attentive and kept her bottle cap filled with fresh water at all times.

Later she took some daytime exploring flights. Much as she liked her new home, she still loved to fly, and longed for the sight and smell of a beach. She even longed for an occasional minnow and getting her feet a little wet. At first Bill was very worried that she wouldn't come back, but every night, just after he had turned on the Dipper sign, Ondine would rap at the door to come in and would strut up and down the counter. She was a great favorite with the customers—mostly truckers—and Bill's diner did a better business than ever.

185

On one of her explorations, Ondine found a wonderful stretch of beach, clean and white, with a grove of trees nearby. Remembering the thrush's description, she flew through the little wood, calling softly, "Mr. Thrush! Oh, Mr. Thrush!"

"Well, bless me!" said a voice. "If it isn't Miss Sandpiper!"

They embraced joyfully, and the thrush said, "I never thought I'd see you again! How did you ever get through that twister alive?"

"I honestly don't know," said Ondine. "But now I don't care. I'm alive and happy—that's what counts! How did you get through?"

The thrush said that just after calling out his warning to Ondine he had dived to earth and luckily found an abandoned gopher hole. "I got into it not a second too soon. The storm hit just after. When it was over I came out, and I looked and looked for you—but I was afraid you were dead. So I decided to come here anyway, in the hope that you might have got through safely and would come here. And here you are! You look wonderful too!"

Ondine laughed and then said, "You were a dear to think of me and remember me. I'll come and see you often."

All that winter Ondine lived happily—the warm sunny days spent at the beach or in the grove talking with the thrush, and the long nights at the Big Dipper Diner. She grew sleek and beautiful, and learned to laugh again—to laugh as she never had before.

Unit Five
Understanding Others

The Art of Henri Rousseau

ERNEST RABOFF

Henri Rousseau was born in Laval, France, in 1844. After a short time in the French army he was married to Clémence Boitard. For the next twenty years he worked as a toll collector but also found time to paint. At the age of forty he retired to become a full-time artist. He gave art and violin lessons for the rest of his life and welcomed all who came to him—rich or poor, famous or unknown. He died in 1910.

Rousseau was a self-taught artist who painted with both inward and outward vision. These bright visions glow for us in every painting.

One of Rousseau's friends wrote that he "was very kind and hospitable. He was happy to receive you even when he was painting. He would ask you to sit down, and keep on working. I was attracted by his calm, his deep satisfaction in his work."

The Toll House, at the right, is a painting of one of the many customhouses where taxes were collected from farmers and merchants as they brought their products into Paris to sell. This may be the very toll house where Rousseau worked for twenty years.

There is both peace and discipline in the picture. The guards stand very stiffly, and the one on the roof can observe things that the guard on the ground cannot see. Even the trees, the two chimneys, and the steeple stand like sentinels. It is a calm, quiet scene.

Working at the toll house was the perfect job for Rousseau. It gave him time to imagine faraway scenes that he could later put into his paintings.

"The Sleeping Gypsy" (1897)   Museum of Modern Art, New York, Gift of Mrs. Simon Guggenheim

The Sleeping Gypsy was described by Rousseau in a letter: "A wandering gypsy who plays the mandolin, with her jar next to her (containing drinking water), is deeply asleep, worn out from fatigue. A lion happens by, sniffs at her, and does not devour her. There is an effect of moonlight, very poetic. The scene takes place in a completely arid desert. The gypsy is dressed in Oriental fashion."

Rousseau, like his gypsy, was a musician who wandered the streets of Paris playing his violin. He would play his music and paint his pictures until he was too tired to continue. Then he would lie down and sleep, believing that his love for nature and for life would always protect him from any harm.

The Waterfall is a great fantasy landscape. At the left of the scene, Rousseau's tall tropical tree with its broad, heart-shaped leaves bends our attention to the rock-bound waterfall, to the men and the two animals. The red-leafed plant is an explosive base for another tree that rises rocket-like, with bold green cone leaves. Hidden in the middle of the jungle, a group of green tepees with decorated tops adds a note of harmony between humans and nature. Rousseau's favorite color, green, dominates the picture. To him it is the color of life. In his imaginary country it is always spring or summer.

The Rooster
That Understood Japanese

YOSHIKO UCHIDA

One of Mrs. Kitamura's pets is Mr. Lincoln, a rooster that understands Japanese. Every afternoon on her way home from school, Miyo visits Mrs. Kitamura. There she is greeted not only by Mr. Lincoln, but also by Mrs. K.'s other animals—Jefferson, a large basset hound, Hamilton, a talkative parrot, and Leonardo, a coal-black cat.

One day Miyo arrives to find Mrs. K. upset and worried because her new neighbor, Mr. Wickett, is going to call the police. Mr. Lincoln, he complains, is disturbing the peace by crowing at six in the morning and waking him up.

Mrs. K. is afraid she will have to give Mr. Lincoln away, but how, she wonders, will she find someone who won't turn him into fricassee or stew?

It is Miyo who finally comes up with a plan that not only saves Mr. Lincoln, but keeps Mrs. K. from becoming a nervous wreck, and changes life for the crabby neighbor as well.

"I know," she said brightly. "I'll put an ad in our class magazine."

Mrs. K. thought about it. "Well," she said slowly, "I suppose it won't do any harm."

What she really meant was that it probably wouldn't do any good either. But Miyo was determined to try. She had to hurry for Mrs. K. had already said several times that she was becoming a nervous wreck, and Miyo certainly didn't want her to stop being the nice, cheerful person she was.

Miyo's class magazine for the month of October was almost ready to be mimeographed. There were several sections, one each for news, feature stories, science,

sports, book reviews, poetry, and, finally, a small section
for ads. That's where Miyo thought Mr. Lincoln would fit
nicely.

She made her ad very special. She wrote, "WANTED:
NICE HOME FOR FRIENDLY, INTELLIGENT, DIGNIFIED ROOSTER. P.S.
HE UNDERSTANDS JAPANESE." Then she added, "PLEASE
HURRY! URGENT!"

Her teacher, Mrs. Fielding, told her it was a fine ad,
and suggested that she include her phone number, so
Miyo did. She also drew a picture of Mr. Lincoln beneath
her ad, trying to make him look dignified and friendly.

The magazine came out on September 30. That very
afternoon, a policeman rang the doorbell of Mrs. K's
house. "I've a complaint, Ma'am," he said, "about a
rooster?" He seemed to think there might have been some
mistake.

Mrs. K. sighed. "Come inside, officer," she said. "I've been expecting you." She supposed now she would just have to go quietly to jail, but first she wanted a cup of tea. "Would you like some tea?" she asked.

Officer McArdle was tired and his feet hurt. "Thank you, Ma'am," he said, and came inside. He looked all around at Mrs. Kitamura's home, bulging with Japanese things he'd never seen before. There were Japanese dolls dancing inside dusty glass cases. There were scrolls of Japanese paintings hanging on the walls. There was the black and gold Buddhist altar, and spread out all over the dining room table were Japanese books and newspapers. Mrs. K. pushed them aside and put down a tray of tea and cookies.

"Dozo," she said, "please have some tea." She took off her apron and smoothed down her hair. Then she told Officer McArdle all about her troubles with Mr. Lincoln.

He looked sympathetic, but he said, "You're breaking a city law by having a rooster in your yard. You really should be fined, you know."

Mrs. K. was astonished. "Even if I am only barely inside the city limits?"

Officer McArdle nodded. "I'm afraid so. I'll give you two more days to get rid of your rooster. Mr. Wickett says you're disturbing the peace." Then he thanked her for the tea and cookies and left.

Miyo was proud of the ad in her class magazine, but no one seemed at all interested in Mr. Lincoln. Instead, several people told her how much they liked her feature story about Mr. Botts, the school custodian, who was retiring.

She had written, "Say good-bye to the best custodian Hawthorn School ever had. Mr. Botts is retiring because he is getting tired. He and Mrs. Botts are going to Far Creek. He is going to eat a lot and sleep a lot and maybe go fishing. So, so long, Mr. Botts. And good luck!"

On her way home, Miyo ran into Mr. Botts himself. He told her it was the first time in his entire life that anyone had written a feature story about him.

When he got home that night, he took off his shoes, sat in his favorite chair, lit a pipe, and read the magazine from cover to cover. At the bottom of page twenty, he saw Miyo's ad about Mr. Lincoln.

"Tami," he said to Mrs. Botts, who happened to be Japanese, "how would you like to have a rooster?"

"A what?"

"A rooster," Mr. Botts repeated. "One that understands Japanese." Mrs. Botts thought that Mr. Botts had had too much excitement, what with his retirement party at school and all. But he kept right on talking.

"When we move to Far Creek, didn't you say you were going to grow vegetables and raise chickens while I go hunting and fishing?"

Mrs. Botts remembered having said something like that. "Yes, I guess I did."

"Well, if you're going to raise chickens, you'll need a rooster."

"Why, I guess that's so."

"Then we might as well have one that's friendly and dignified," Mr. Botts said, and he went right to the telephone to call Miyo.

"I'll take that rooster you want to find a home for," he said. "My wife, Tami, could talk to it in Japanese too."

Miyo couldn't believe it. Someone had actually read her ad and that someone was Mr. Botts. He and his wife would give Mr. Lincoln a fine home and surely wouldn't turn him into fricassee or stew. At last, she had done something to help Mrs. K. and keep her from becoming a nervous wreck. As soon as she told Mother, she ran right over to tell Mrs. K. the good news.

Mrs. K. was just about to stuff Mr. Lincoln into a wooden crate for the night. When Miyo told her that Mr. Lincoln would have a nice half-Japanese home in Far Creek with Mr. and Mrs. Botts, Mrs. K. gave Miyo such a hug she almost squeezed the breath out of her.

"Hooray! *Banzai!*" Mrs. K. said happily. "Tomorrow we will have a party to celebrate. I shall invite you and your mama, and Mr. and Mrs. Botts." And because Mrs. K. felt so relieved and happy, she even decided to invite Mr. Wickett.

"Even though you are a cross old man," she said to him, "I suppose you were right. A rooster shouldn't live in a small pen at the edge of town. He should live in the country where he'll have some hens to talk to and nobody will care if he crows at the sun."

Mr. Wickett was a little embarrassed to come to Mrs. K's party, but he was too lonely to say no. He came with a box of chocolate-dipped cherries and said, "I'm sorry I caused such a commotion."

But Mrs. K. told him he needn't be sorry. "Life needs a little stirring up now and then," she admitted. "Besides," she added, "now both Mr. Lincoln and I have found new friends."

Miyo and her mother brought a caramel cake with Mr. Lincoln's initials on it, and Mr. and Mrs. Botts brought Mrs. K. a philodendron plant. "Maybe you can talk to it in Japanese now instead of to Mr. Lincoln," Mrs. Botts said, "and don't worry, I'll take good care of him."

"You come on out to visit us and your rooster any time you like," Mr. Botts added.

Miyo's mother promised that one day soon she would drive them all up to Far Creek to see how Mr. Lincoln liked his new home.

When the party was over, Mr. Botts carried Mr. Lincoln in his crate to his station wagon. Mr. Lincoln gave a polite squawk of farewell and Mrs. K. promised she would come visit him soon.

"Good-bye, Mr. Lincoln. Good-bye, Mr. and Mrs. Botts," Miyo called.

198

From inside Mrs. K's kitchen, Hamilton, the parrot, screeched. "Good-bye, Mr. Lincoln. Good-bye." Jefferson roused himself from his bed near the stove and came outside to wag his tail at everybody, and Leonardo rubbed up against Mrs. K's legs to remind her that he was still there. Then Mr. Botts honked his horn and they were gone.

"I hope we'll see each other again soon," Mr. Wickett said to Mrs. K.

"Good night, Mr. Wickett," she answered. "I'm sure we will."

Miyo and her mother thanked Mrs. K. for the nice party and went home. "Do you think she'll miss Mr. Lincoln a lot?" Miyo asked.

"She will for a while," Mother answered, "but now she has a new friend and neighbor to talk to."

Miyo nodded. That was true. And even if Mr. Wickett couldn't understand Japanese, at least he could answer back. Maybe that was even better than having an intelligent rooster around. She was glad everything had turned out so well, and went to bed feeling good inside.

"Good night, Mama," she called softly to her mother.

"Good night, Miyo," Mother answered.

Then, one by one, the lights went out in all the houses along the street, and soon only the sounds of the insects filled the dark night air.

The Tiger

Tiger! Tiger! burning bright
In the forests of the night,
What immortal hand or eye
Could frame thy fearful symmetry?

In what distant deeps or skies
Burnt the fire of thine eyes?
On what wings dare he aspire?
What the hand dare seize the fire?

When the stars threw down their spears
And watered heaven with their tears,
Did he smile his work to see?
Did he who made the Lamb make thee?

Tiger! Tiger! burning bright
In the forests of the night,
What immortal hand or eye
Dare frame thy fearful symmetry?

—William Blake

The Castle on Hester Street

LINDA HELLER

One day while Julie was visiting her grandparents, her grandfather said, "Did I ever tell you about my good friend Moishe?"

"You told me about Hershel, the famous astronomer," Julie said with a giggle, "the one who discovered that the moon is a matzah ball. And you told me about Bessie, your little cousin whose braids were so long she used them for jump ropes. But you never told me about Moishe."

"Moishe the goat was from my village in Russia," Julie's grandfather said. "He pulled the wagon I rode in when I came to America. Not only could Moishe leap across oceans the way others jump over puddles, but he also could sing. We started singing the moment we left Russia: '9,092 miles to go, 9,092 miles; after we pass that small patch of snow, we'll have 9,091 miles to go.' "

Julie was about to join in, when her grandmother said, "Sol, what are you telling that child?"

201

"A true story, just the way I remember it, Rose dear," Julie's grandfather said. "Moishe's wagon was solid gold. It shone like a shooting star when we flew over the ocean."

"That's a story, all right, but it's not true!" Julie's grandmother said. "Grandpa came on a boat, just as I did. It was terrible. Hundreds of families were crowded together. Babies were crying. Bundles were piled all over. The boat rocked so much I thought we would drown. But in Russia, life for Jews was very hard. We couldn't live or work where we wanted. Sometimes we were attacked just because we were Jews. We had to leave Russia any way we could."

As her grandmother spoke, pictures grew in Julie's mind of her grandparents leaving their country and crossing a rough winter ocean on a boat so crowded they could hardly move.

"Grandpa, is that how you really came?" Julie asked, looking sad.

"Yes, it was," Julie's grandfather said. He, too, looked sad, until he added, "But what a welcome I got when I arrived. President Theodore Roosevelt rode his horse through a blizzard of ticker tape to greet me. 'Hello, Sol,' he said. 'Mighty glad you could come.' "

"Don't listen to another word," Julie's grandmother said. "Grandpa's brother Morris met him. The boat docked first at Ellis Island. We sat for hours and waited to be inspected. Not everyone who came could stay. If you were sick, you had to go back. I was so afraid they would find something wrong with me, but, thank God, I passed every test."

"Hooray!" Julie shouted.

"Thank you, dear," Julie's grandmother said. She gave her a kiss and said, "I have something to show you." Then she went to the closet.

Julie's grandfather leaned closer and whispered to Julie, "Everyone who came here was given a castle. Mine was on Hester Street. It was so tall the pigeons couldn't fly all the way up to the roof. I had to carry them there."

Julie's grandmother came back to the sofa carrying a box. "Did grandpa tell you about the horrible little room he shared with Louie, the cigarmaker, and Herman, the tailor?" she asked as she sat down. "In those days people had to take in boarders to help pay the rent.

Life was hard. Grandpa had a pushcart. He sold buttons fourteen hours a day, six days a week. The only rest he got was on the Sabbath."

"Poor grandpa," Julie said, and she patted his hand.

Julie's grandfather was quiet for a moment, then he said, "But what buttons I had! Buttons carved from diamonds, emeralds, and rubies. Buttons as big as saucers. Buttons as big as plates. Buttons you could use as sleds in the snow."

Julie's grandmother sighed loudly. "Grandpa sold small buttons, small enough to fit through buttonholes. I'll show you," she said as she opened the box. The box was filled with photographs. Julie's grandmother took out an old photograph in a cardboard frame. In it Julie's grandfather stood next to his pushcart, which was full of little buttons.

"Grandpa looks so strong," Julie said, feeling proud.

Julie's grandfather found a photograph of a young girl and showed it to Julie. "This is a picture of your grandmother," he

said. "She was very famous in those days. Everyone spoke of Mr. Witkin's beautiful daughter Rose, who stayed home all day nibbling chocolates. Her five big brothers had to watch so that nobody stole her away."

"I worked six days a week in a factory then, sewing dresses. But I was very pretty," Julie's grandmother said, smoothing her hair.

"You are still very pretty," Julie's grandfather said, and he kissed her cheek.

"In Russia your grandmother sewed for royalty. She made stitches so small they couldn't be seen. People wondered how the dresses stayed together."

"That part is true," Julie's grandmother said proudly.

"As soon as I met your grandmother, I wanted to marry her," Julie's grandfather said. "Every night I hired fireflies to fly over her house and spell out 'Rose, my precious flower, I love you every hour.' And Moishe and I sang love songs under her window.

"Finally her father let me marry her. A year later your mother was born. No one had ever seen such a beautiful child. Then Esther, Ruthie, and Bennie were born, and they were just as beautiful. I made them tiny jeweled crowns, and they rode through the streets in hand-carved, golden baby carriages."

"Enough is enough," Julie's grandmother said. "From now on I insist that Julie hear only the truth. Grandpa and I had to work even harder to feed all those babies, but we didn't mind. We had something more valuable than jeweled crowns and golden baby carriages. We had each other, and we were free to live as we wanted."

"That's the truth, Rose dear," Julie's grandfather said. "And from now on that's all that will pass through my lips."

They sat quietly for a few minutes. Then Julie's grandfather smiled and whispered to Julie, "Did I ever tell you about the time Moishe the goat and I sang for President Wilson?"

My Hot Get Feet

My hot get feet
When I beat the drum.
No—my feet get drum
When I hot the beat.
No—my beat gets hot
When I feet the drum.
No—my drum gets hot
When I beat the feet.
No—my feet get beat
When my drum gets hot.
Oh, never mind—forget the heat.
My feet are cold and I am beat.

—Dean Hughes

205

Choosing Shoes

New shoes, new shoes,
  Red and pink and blue shoes.
Tell me, what would *you* choose,
  If they'd let us buy?

Buckle shoes, bow shoes,
  Pretty pointy-toe shoes,
Strappy, cappy low shoes;
  Let's have some to try.

Bright shoes, white shoes,
  Dandy-dance-by-night shoes,
Perhaps-a-little-tight shoes,
  Like some? So would I.

            But

Flat shoes, fat shoes,
  Stump-along-like-that shoes,
Wipe-them-on-the-mat shoes,
  That's the sort they'll buy.

                    —Ffrida Wolfe

Anna's Silent World

BERNARD WOLF

This is Anna. She lives in New York City with her mother and father, her brother, Danny, and her sister, Suzi.

Most mornings when Anna wakes up the first thing she sees is her cat, Tycho. When Anna touches him she can feel his rumbling purr. Without special help Anna cannot hear the sound of Tycho's purr or her dog Homer's bark or her brother's violin. Anna was born deaf.

But Anna is learning to talk and to read and write the way people around her do. Her family, her close friends, and the boys and girls she goes to school with all have normal hearing. The world that is silent for Anna is the same one that is full of sound for almost everyone she knows.

She receives special training to overcome her deafness at the New York League for the Hard of Hearing. Here, Dr. Jane R. Madell gives Anna a yearly test to see if there have been any changes in her ability to hear. Anna can hear almost nothing. However, like most deaf people, Anna can hear some sounds. At the League she is learning to use what little hearing she has.

The loudness of sound is measured in decibels. One decibel is very soft and the numbers go up as the sound gets louder. Most people can hear a sound when it is between one and twenty-five decibels. A sound must be very loud—at least ninety decibels—before Anna can hear it when she is not wearing her hearing aids. With the aids she hears some sounds at fifty-five decibels.

Learning how to talk and to lip-read are the hardest parts of Anna's training. Even when the sound is amplified, she can hear only parts of the words spoken to her.

We hear because sound makes our ear drums vibrate and the auditory nerves carry sound sensations to the brain. Anna's auditory nerves do not work as they should. To help Anna hear, a vibrator is placed on her wrist and connected to the amplifier. When the teacher speaks into the microphone, sound is conducted through the bones of Anna's wrist and arm. This reinforces what Anna hears through the earphones and helps her learn to use her whole body to hear sounds.

It is especially important for Anna to learn to pronounce words correctly so that other people can understand what she says. Using only the hearing aids she wears every day, Anna practices words that have a certain sound such as the "t" (tuh) sound at the beginning, middle, or end. She spins the dial and makes a sentence using the

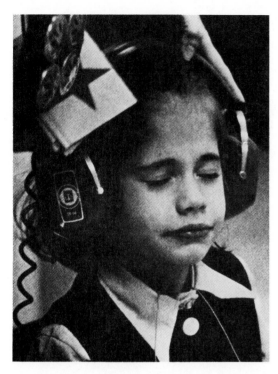

name of the object that the dial points to.

Anna has been working with people at the New York League for the Hard of Hearing since she was two years old. The League believes that the best way to help the deaf is to teach them how to communicate by listening and speaking the way people with normal hearing do.

Anna uses what she learns all the time. She goes to St. Luke's School near her home. For her, school is a happy place where she loves to find out about new things.

Anna's best friend, Margaret Pardo, sometimes comes to spend Saturday afternoons with her. But Margaret doesn't always understand Anna clearly. Once Anna's mother came into the room just as Anna was trying to repeat herself.

"Sometimes it's hard for me to figure out what Anna is saying," Margaret said.

"That's because Anna is still learning how to speak clearly," Anna's mother explained. "Deaf children need to hear a word hundreds of times before they can use it the way you and I do. Even with her hearing aids, Anna hears much less than you do. It will take her longer to speak clearly, but she'll catch up. By the time the two of you are in high school, her speech will be almost like anyone else's."

"Well, most of the time I know what she's saying," Margaret said. "The thing is, if she can't hear me, how does she know what *I'm* saying?"

"Anna has to look at you and read your lips to hear, and her hearing aids help. Let me show you."

Anna's mother showed Margaret the two amplifiers that Anna wears strapped to her chest under her shirt. The amplifiers are powered by batteries and a wire runs from each of them to the earpieces. When the amplifiers are turned on, they make sounds louder and Anna can hear more than she can without them.

Anna sometimes lets Margaret listen with one of her hearing aids. For a moment, a friend shares Anna's silent world.

Santiago's Silver Mine

ELEANOR CLYMER

Santiago and his friend Andreas live in a village in Mexico called San Juan de la Montaña. The harvest has been bad, so their fathers have gone away to work in Mexico City. The boys earn some money by showing strangers the village's beautiful church or by leading them to the abandoned silver mine where José, the grouchy caretaker, shows them around.

But Andreas dreams of finding treasure or looking for silver in the old mine. He has hopes of becoming rich, although Santiago doubts that this will happen.

One day when the boys are watching Señor Salvador's cow near the mine, she wanders away. They follow her and Andreas makes a discovery.

Santiago is telling the story.

Andreas said, "Wait!"

"What's the matter?" I asked.

"I found something," he said. "Tie the cow to a tree and come down here."

I tied her so that she could go on eating but couldn't get away, and followed Andreas down the path. I heard him, but I couldn't see him. "Where are you?" I called.

"Down here, below the rocks," he said.

Then I saw that there was a ledge of rock sticking out of the hillside like a roof. Andreas was underneath it. I went down to him.

"Look what I found," he said. There was an old shovel with a broken handle and a hole where somebody had been digging. Andreas was on his hands and knees, feeling in the dirt with his fingers. "I found something,"

211

he said. And he held up a broken piece of a clay cup. It was black, with a streak of red paint. He looked at it with disgust. "I thought I would find something good," he said.

I started to dig too. Soon I found another piece like the first one. But then Andreas took the shovel, in order to dig faster. "I've got something!" he said, and then he gave a yell. It was a bone! There was a skeleton there! "*Caramba!*" he shouted. "Let's get out of here! Somebody's been murdered!"

But I said, "No, I don't think so. These are old bones. I think somebody was buried here very long ago."

Then I picked out from the dirt a little thing that looked like a doll made of clay. I dug some more. I found a bowl with three legs, and some broken pieces, and then a jar. It was shaped like a bird, the lower part round, and a small round part stuck on top for a head. The head was painted with two big eyes and a beak.

212

"It looks like an owl," I said. But Andreas was not interested in broken dishes or even in owls. He had discovered something else.

"See," he said, "there is a path leading down to the mine. This is the way to get there, not over the wall. Now is our chance to see what's there. I'm going down."

"No, don't," I said. But he was scrambling down the hill. I called, "Come back!" But he wouldn't, so I had to go with him.

Andreas walked straight to the mine door and slid back the bolt. It moved easily, as if it had been oiled. We looked in. It was dark and smelled of musty earth, and I could dimly see the tunnel stretching away into the blackness. For a minute I thought of my grandfather, going in there every day, and it made me shiver.

Andreas took a step forward, as if he were going in, but I pulled him back and said, "No, don't go in."

213

"But I want to see if there's treasure," he said.

"Look there," I told him. Just inside the door was a basket, and in it were some more of the little clay dolls, and a couple of three-legged bowls.

He said, "You mean this is it?"

I said, "Yes. I saw one of those in the market, in a lady's bag. It was one of those little dolls. José must have sold it to her. He's the one who has been digging, and selling what he finds. Come on. Let's go, before he comes back."

I pushed the door shut and we ran back to the hill and climbed as fast as we could. I felt scared, as though something were chasing me. We untied the cow and led her back over the hill to the pasture, and tied her so she would not break through the fence again. Then we sat down to catch our breath.

"What a strange thing," said Andreas. "All the time I thought there would be silver or money."

"Silver or money would be different," I said. "But I don't think it's right to dig where somebody is buried. I don't know."

"What shall we do?" he asked.

I said, "We must talk to the teacher. He will know."

Then we went to the teacher's house. He was starting to eat his supper. He said, "Come in, boys. You haven't been to school lately. What have you been doing?"

I said, "We were working because our fathers have gone away. And today, when we were guarding *Señor* Salvador's cow, we found something. We thought you would know what it is." And I took out the little doll.

The teacher jumped up as if a bee had stung him. "*Esto es increíble!*" he shouted. "Where did you find this?"

"Up over the hill," I told him. "We were following the cow, and there are some rocks there. We saw that somebody had been digging, so we dug too, and we found this and some broken dishes and some bones."

"But this is tremendous!" he said. "It must be a burial. This is very old. Who knows? You may have made a discovery."

Andreas said, "What is it? Isn't it just a doll?"

The teacher answered, "No, Andreas, it's an idol, a little image of a god, perhaps. The people used to put these into the graves to help the dead on their way to the next world. And they left bowls with food and jars with flowers or water."

"What were the jars like?" I asked.

"Sometimes they had faces," he said. "Sometimes they were shaped like animals or birds. But why are we sitting here? You must take me there at once. Nobody must dig any more. We must get an archaeologist from the city. Nothing must be moved."

I said, "But, *Señor*, some things have already been moved. José has taken some. We looked in the mine itself and found more of them in a basket."

216

"It's against the law," said the teacher. "These are our national treasures."

Andreas said, "Señor, you told us there were no treasures around here. We were looking for treasure, but we didn't know that little clay dolls and broken dishes were so valuable."

The teacher sat down again. He wiped his face with his handkerchief and calmed down a little.

Then he said, "When I said that, I meant there were no great pyramids or magnificent carvings. But you see, here and there we find the places where plain, simple people lived, people like you and me. They lived and died and were buried, and from the burials we learn about them. We learn how they lived, what they ate, what they believed. They were our ancestors. But to study them, we must find them where they are lying. That's why it is wrong to dig these things out and sell them. Now come, we must go."

217

We wanted to take the teacher over the hill the way we went, but he said, "No, it is better to go to José directly." So we went along the path and banged on the door. We had to bang a long time, but at last José came. Andreas and I were scared, but the teacher was not afraid at all.

He said, "Señor, I am sorry to disturb you, but it has come to my notice that there may be an ancient burial somewhere here. Can you tell me about it?"

José said, "This is the property of the mine owners. Nobody is allowed here. Nobody could have found anything here."

"Except you, Señor," said the teacher. "I am glad to hear it. You know it is against the law to dig or sell ancient things. Of course you would not break the law."

"Me?" shouted José. "Are you accusing me?"

"No. I am asking you to help me," said the teacher.

So we went in, and José scowled at us, but he couldn't prevent us from showing the teacher where to look. First he looked inside the mine entrance. José didn't want him to open the door, but he did anyhow, and there was the basket.

The teacher picked it up and said, "Señor, I see you understand the value of these things and have taken good care of them. I will take them with me to be sure nothing happens to them."

And he carefully put the little dolls and the bowls in a box that he had with him. José looked angry, but he didn't say a word. Then we went up the path and pointed out the place under the rock ledge. The teacher had a little shovel, and he began to dig, very carefully. He got so excited that I was afraid he would fall down the hill.

218

He found the skeleton, but did not touch it. Instead he covered it up again. Then he picked out a bowl that had some little bits of bone in the bottom.

"See," he said, "This was meat that was put there for this person to eat on his journey. The bowl is a type that was made more than two thousand years ago. *Muchachos*, it is a great discovery."

He carefully covered everything up, and we went back down the path. José asked, "Well, *Señor*, did you find anything?"

"Yes," said the teacher, "some ancient bones and pottery of much value. And now I must go to town to telephone. We will get an expert from the city to come and work here, and we will get the police to come and guard the place, so that nothing happens to it. And meanwhile you, *Señor*, can see that nobody comes near, so that nothing is disturbed. And now good morning."

José said, "But what about those things you took? Are you going to keep them?"

The teacher said, "I will show them to the authorities. Perhaps you will get a reward when I explain that you found them." We went out and heard the bolt slide shut.

The teacher got his car, and we went with him to town. It was a good ride. He drove very fast and almost hit a few things, but we got there safely. He telephoned and then started back.

I said, "But you said you were going to the police, Señor."

He laughed. "That was just to frighten José. I do not think we will need the police." And sure enough, when we returned and went back to the mine, the door was not locked. We went in and found nobody. José was gone.

Some archaeologists came from the museum in the city, and they examined everything, and then they decided to dig on the hillside. But first some workers

came to fix the road so that cars could come in. And best of all, my father and Andreas's father came home. They got jobs on the road, and later at the dig.

The archaeologists said it was a good dig, because they found things that showed how the people lived—tools and pottery and even some bits of cloth and basketwork.

They worked most of the winter, until it was time for planting again. Andreas and I worked there too, when we were not in school. We carried water to the diggers, and helped them carry away dirt. I learned the right way to dig, very carefully so as not to spoil anything, but to uncover everything just as it lay in the earth. I like this work. I hope the diggers will come back. Maybe when I grow up I'll be an archaeologist.

New Land, New Ways

BETTY LEE SUNG

For people who have to pull up roots and leave their homes and friends, moving to a foreign land is a very painful experience. When they arrive in a new country, they want to live in a place where the faces and way of life will be like those they have left behind. That is why they are drawn to places where other people from the old country have settled. This is true of immigrants from China today as well as of all the other immigrants who have come to this country.

Today's Chinese immigrants are usually educated or have special skills. Their biggest problem is that many do not know how to speak, read, or write the English language. Therefore, they feel afraid to go far from the Chinese community. To understand the feeling of these newcomers, imagine that your family has moved to China. Your parents would have to earn a living, although they spoke and understood no Chinese. Your family would have to get used to living in a Chinese-style house and to shopping in the open market, where you may never find bread, steak, breakfast cereals, or milk. These foods are not commonly eaten in China. Instead, you would have to get used to rice, salt fish, bitter melons, *bok choy*, and bean curd—foods common to the Chinese diet.

If you walked into a classroom where all your schoolmates looked different and wore clothes unlike your own, you would feel out of place. If the teacher started reading from a book that was written in little square characters, and if you could not make out one word that he or she was saying, you would feel very unhappy until you were able to pick up a little of the Chinese language. If every time you spoke (in order to show that you were trying to learn the language and to prove that you could say a few words) your classmates laughed because you could not pronounce Chinese the way they did, you would feel very hurt. If your playmates made fun of you and would not let you join their games, you would feel very left out.

Similarly, Chinese children who come to this country face special problems. They have to get used to their new surroundings and to a new school. They have to try to make new friends. They have to spend more time at their homework. If they cannot speak or read well in English, their teachers may think they are poor learners.

The Chinese are very proud of their civilization and culture. Many parents send their children to Chinese school so that they can learn the language and the history of China. Giving their children knowledge of their past is like giving them the most valuable riches. And the key to these riches is the language.

At Chinese school, the students learn to read and write characters like the ones shown on page 225. Each character is a squarish-shaped one-syllable word. Chinese started out as a picture language. A picture was drawn to represent a thing or an idea. With more than 4000 years of history, there is a rich body of literature written in the Chinese language.

People from all parts of the world have developed different ways of expressing themselves. There must be thousands of different ways of saying "dog," or "friend," or "eat." When we say "friend" and the other person does not understand, then there is a language barrier. There is something in the way of our communicating, even though we are standing together, face-to-face.

There are other ways that people get across their ideas. Body language is just as important a form of communication as words are. And it, too, differs from country to country. For instance, when people greet each other in the United States, they shake hands. Americans may feel hurt or offended when they put out a hand to

練習　四

把下面的字重新組織成句

一　島上各的各種樣著海島。

二　到奇觀處有都海的潮。

三　這為個島居住人不許民。

四　美洲是實在觀潮在所的最好。

五　虎正獅在演衰跳火的圈戲遊。

六　大象作耤滑樣的子出種種。

shake the hand of someone they have just met if the other person does not also put out a hand. But French people may kiss each other on both cheeks in greeting. The Chinese bow slightly and shake their own hands. These different customs are a form of language.

New Chinese immigrants come to the United States with some of these cultural differences. They have to learn both a verbal language and a body language, and they have to learn them quickly in order to survive. In the Chinese community, their own people can help them because they understand the problem. After a while the situation will improve, but at the beginning the adjustment is a trying experience.

The Mouse and the Motorcycle

BEVERLY CLEARY

A young mouse named Ralph lives with his family in a mousehole in a room in the Mountain View Inn. His life is suddenly changed when a boy named Keith moves into the room. Keith has a toy motorcycle just the right size for a mouse. When Keith leaves the room, Ralph cannot resist climbing onto the bedside table and getting on the motorcycle. Soon he and Keith meet, and the boy allows him to ride the motorcycle outside the room. But this is the beginning of trouble, for Ralph soon loses the toy.

It was a sad night for Ralph, a sad and lonely night. If he went back to the mousehole, his mother was sure to worry him with embarrassing questions about the motorcycle. She would also expect him to help clean up after the family reunion. If he took off his crash helmet, he could squeeze under the door and explore the hall on foot, but he could not bear to part with the helmet and, anyway, he had no desire to travel by foot where he had once ridden with such noise and speed.

Ralph scurried through shadows on the floor to the curtain, which he climbed to the windowsill. There he sat, huddled and alone, staring out into the night listening to the kissing sounds of the bats as they jerked and zigzagged from the eaves of the hotel, through the pines and back again. Around the window the leaves of a Virginia creeper vine shifted in the breeze, and down in the lobby a clock struck midnight. An owl slid silently through the night across the clearing of the parking lot from one pine to another. Ralph could remember a time when he had envied bats and owls their ability to fly, but that was before he had experienced the speed and power of a motorcycle.

Early in the morning the smell of bacon drifting up from the kitchen brought back all Ralph's dreams of the ground floor. It was not long until he was embarrassed to discover that Keith was awake and was lying quietly in bed watching him.

"Hi," said Keith.

"Oh, hello." Ralph wished he had returned to the mousehole before dawn. "Well, I guess it's about time for me to go home to bed."

Keith sat up. "Don't go yet. Wait until my folks get up."

Ralph leaped to the floor. "I didn't think you would want to talk to me after I lost your motorcycle."

"I may never have another chance to talk to a mouse."

Ralph was flattered. It had never occurred to him that a boy would consider talking to a mouse anything special.

"What would you like for breakfast?" asked Keith.

"You mean we still get room service? After what I did?"

227

"Sure." Keith pulled his knees up under his chin and wrapped his arms around his legs.

"You mean you aren't mad at me anymore?" asked Ralph.

"I guess you might say I'm mad but not *real* mad," Keith decided. "I've been lying here thinking. It wouldn't be right for me to be *real* mad, because I get into messes myself. My mom and dad tell me I don't stop to use my head."

Ralph nodded. "I guess that's my trouble, too. I don't stop to use my head."

"They say I'm in too much of a hurry," said Keith. "They say I don't want to take time to learn to do things properly."

Ralph nodded again. He understood. If he had waited until he had learned to ride the motorcycle he would never have ridden off the bedside table into the wastebasket.

"I'll never forget the first time I rode a bicycle with hand brakes," reminisced Keith. "I took right off down a hill. I had always ridden bicycles with foot brakes and when I got going too fast I tried to put on foot brakes only there weren't any."

"What happened?" Ralph was fascinated.

"By the time I remembered to use the hand brakes I hit a tree and took an awful spill."

Somehow, this story made Ralph feel better. He was not the only one who got into trouble.

"The hard part is," continued Keith, "I *am* in a hurry. I don't want to do kid things. I want to do big things. Real things. I want to grow up."

"You look pretty grown-up to me," said Ralph.

"Maybe to a mouse," conceded Keith, "but I want to look grown-up to grownups."

"So do I," said Ralph with feeling. "I want to grow up and go down to the ground floor."

"Everybody tells me to be patient," said Keith, "but I don't want to be patient."

"Me neither," agreed Ralph. Someone stirred next door in room 216. "Well, I guess I better be running along," said Ralph. "Say, about that breakfast—"

"Sure. What do you want?"

"How about some bacon?" suggested Ralph, remembering the fragrance that had floated up to the windowsill.

"And some toast?"

"With jelly," agreed Ralph and ran off to the mousehole, eager to tell his family things were not so bad after all. They were still entitled to room service.

229

I'm Nobody

I'm nobody! Who are you?
Are you nobody too?
Then there's a pair of us—don't tell!
They'd banish us, you know.

How dreary to be somebody!
How public, like a frog
To tell your name the livelong day
To an admiring bog.

—Emily Dickinson

Ruth and Naomi

Retold by ALVIN TRESSELT

In the days when the Judges ruled Israel, there was a famine in the land. A certain man named Elimelech, who lived in Bethlehem, in Judah, went with his wife, Naomi, and their two sons to live in the country of Moab, because there was food in that land.

In time Elimelech, Naomi's husband, died, and her two sons took wives. They were women of Moab. The name of one was Orpah, and the name of the other was Ruth. And Naomi and her sons and their wives lived in Moab for about ten years.

It came to pass that both sons died. Naomi was alone in a strange land with her daughters-in-law. She now prepared to return to her own country, for she heard that there was once more food in the land of Judah. Orpah and Ruth set out with Naomi to see that she was well started on her journey. At last it was time for them to part, and Naomi said to her daughters-in-law, "Return now each of you to your mother's house. May the Lord be as kind to you as you have been to me and to my sons."

The women wept together, and Orpah returned to her mother's house. But Ruth clung to Naomi and said, "Do not ask me to leave you. Wherever you go, I shall go. Where you stop, there will I stop also. Your people shall be my people, and your God shall be my God."

Naomi, seeing that she could not persuade Ruth to go back, permitted her to continue on to Bethlehem.

It was the time of the barley harvest, and Ruth said, "Let me go into the fields that I may follow after the reapers and glean the ears of grain which they have passed over. In this way we will have food to eat."

It happened that Ruth was gleaning in a field that belonged to a wealthy kinsman of Naomi's named Boaz. When Boaz saw Ruth, he asked his servants who she was. The servant replied that she was Ruth, who had returned with Naomi from the country of Moab.

Then Boaz spoke to Ruth. He told her that she might glean freely from his fields and drink the water from his

well. And he instructed the servants to let her glean even among the sheaves of gathered barley and to let grain fall on the ground so that she would find enough.

When Ruth returned that night to Naomi, she told her what had happened, and Naomi was joyful, for Boaz was a kinsman. So it was throughout all the barley harvest and the wheat harvest. Ruth gleaned every day with the servants of Boaz.

At last when the harvest was done, Boaz went before the elders of the city and declared his wish to make Ruth his wife, and the elders blessed the marriage.

And the son of Ruth and Boaz was Obed. His son was Jesse, the father of David, who became King of Israel.

The Cowardly Lion

L. FRANK BAUM

A whirlwind has carried Dorothy and her dog Toto far away from Kansas to the Land of Oz. Dorothy wants to find her way home. A good witch has told her to follow the yellow brick road to Emerald City, where the Great Wizard of Oz will help her. On her way to the Emerald City Dorothy has met a Scarecrow and a Tin Woodman. Both have decided to travel with her.

All this time Dorothy and her companions had been walking through the thick woods. The road was still paved with yellow bricks, but these were much covered by dried branches and dead leaves from the trees, and the walking was not at all good.

There were few birds in this part of the forest, for birds love the open country where there is plenty of sunshine. But now and then there came a deep growl from some wild animal hidden among the trees. These sounds made the little girl's heart beat fast, for she did not know what made them. But Toto knew, and he walked close to Dorothy's side, and did not even bark in return.

"How long will it be," Dorothy asked the Tin Woodman, "before we are out of the forest?"

"I cannot tell," was the answer, "for I have never been to the Emerald City. But my father went there once, when I was a boy. He said it was a long journey through a dangerous country, although nearer to the city where Oz dwells the country is beautiful. But I am not afraid so long as I have my oilcan, and nothing can hurt the Scarecrow, while you bear upon your forehead the mark of the good Witch's kiss, and that will protect you from harm."

"But Toto!" said the girl anxiously, "what will protect him?"

"We must protect him ourselves, if he is in danger," replied the Tin Woodman.

Just as he spoke there came from the forest a terrible roar, and the next moment a great Lion bounded into the road. With one blow of his paw he sent the Scarecrow spinning over and over to the edge of the road, and then he struck at the Tin Woodman with his sharp claws. But, to the Lion's surprise, he could make no impression on the tin, although the Woodman fell over in the road and lay still.

Little Toto, now that he had an enemy to face, ran barking toward the Lion, and the great beast opened his mouth to bite the dog. Dorothy, fearing Toto would be killed, and heedless of danger, rushed forward and slapped the Lion upon his nose as hard as she could, while she cried out,

"Don't you dare bite Toto! You ought to be ashamed of yourself, a big beast like you, to bite a poor little dog!"

"I didn't bite him," said the Lion, as he rubbed his nose with his paw where Dorothy had hit it.

"No, but you tried to," she retorted. "You are nothing but a big coward."

"I know it," said the Lion, hanging his head in shame. "I've always known it. But how can I help it?"

"I don't know, I'm sure. To think of your striking a stuffed man like the poor Scarecrow!"

"Is he stuffed?" asked the Lion in surprise, as he watched her pick up the Scarecrow and set him upon his feet, while she patted him into shape again.

"Of course he's stuffed," replied Dorothy, who was still angry.

"That's why he went over so easily," remarked the Lion. "It astonished me to see him whirl around so. Is the other one stuffed also?"

"No," said Dorothy, "he's made of tin." And she helped the Woodman up again.

"That's why he nearly blunted my claws," said the Lion. "When they scratched against the tin, it made a cold shiver run down my back. What is that little animal you are so tender of?"

"He is my dog, Toto," answered Dorothy.

"Is he made of tin or stuffed?" asked the Lion.

"Neither. He's a—a—a meat dog," said the girl.

"Oh. He's a curious animal and seems remarkably small, now that I look at him. No one would think of biting such a little thing except a coward like me," continued the Lion sadly.

"What makes you a coward?" asked Dorothy, looking at the great beast in wonder, for he was as big as a small horse.

"It's a mystery," replied the Lion. "I suppose I was born that way. All the other animals in the forest naturally expect me to be brave, for the Lion is everywhere thought to be the King of Beasts. I learned that if I roared very loudly, every living thing was frightened and got out of my way.

237

Whenever I've met a person I've been awfully scared, but I just roar, and they always run away as fast as they can go. If the elephants and the tigers and the bears had ever tried to fight me, I should have run myself—I'm such a coward. But just as soon as they hear me roar, they all try to get away from me, and of course I let them go."

"But that isn't right. The King of Beasts shouldn't be a coward," said the Scarecrow.

"I know it," returned the Lion, wiping a tear from his eye with the tip of his tail. "It is my great sorrow and makes my life very unhappy. But whenever there is danger, my heart begins to beat fast."

"Perhaps you have heart disease," said the Tin Woodman.

"It may be," said the Lion.

"If you have," continued the Tin Woodman, "you ought to be glad, for it proves you have a heart. For my part, I have no heart, so I cannot have heart disease."

"Perhaps," said the Lion thoughtfully, "if I had no heart I should not be a coward."

"Have you brains?" asked the Scarecrow.

"I suppose so. I've never looked to see," replied the Lion.

"I am going to the great Oz to ask him to give me some," remarked the Scarecrow, "for my head is stuffed with straw."

"And I am going to ask him to give me a heart," said the Woodman.

"And I am going to ask him to send Toto and me back to Kansas," added Dorothy.

"Do you think Oz could give me courage?" asked the Cowardly Lion.

"Just as easily as he could give me brains," said the Scarecrow.

"Or give me a heart," said the Tin Woodman.

"Or send me back to Kansas," said Dorothy.

"Then, if you don't mind, I'll go with you," said the Lion, "for my life is simply unbearable without a bit of courage."

"You will be very welcome," answered Dorothy, "for you will help to keep away the other wild beasts. It seems to me they must be more cowardly than you are if they allow you to scare them so easily."

"They really are," said the Lion. "But that doesn't make me any braver, and as long as I know myself to be a coward I shall be unhappy."

So once more the little company set off upon the journey, the Lion walking with stately strides at Dorothy's side. Toto did not approve this new comrade at first, for he could not forget how nearly he had been crushed between the Lion's great jaws. But after a time he became more at ease, and presently Toto and the Cowardly Lion had grown to be good friends.

During the rest of that day there was no other adventure to mar the peace of their journey. Once, indeed, the Tin Woodman stepped upon a beetle that was crawling along the road, and killed the poor little thing. This made the Tin Woodman very unhappy, for he was always careful not to hurt any living creature. As he walked along, he wept several tears of sorrow and regret. These tears ran slowly down his face and over the hinges of his jaw, and there they rusted. When Dorothy presently asked him a question, the Tin Woodman could not open his mouth, for his jaws were tightly rusted together. He became greatly frightened at this and made many motions to Dorothy to help him, but she could not understand. The Lion was also puzzled to know what was wrong. But the Scarecrow seized the oilcan from Dorothy's basket and oiled the Woodman's jaws, so that after a few moments he could talk as well as before.

"This will serve me a lesson," said he, "to look where I step. For if I should kill another bug or beetle, it would make me feel so bad that I should surely cry again, and crying rusts my jaws so that I cannot speak."

Thereafter he walked very carefully, with his eyes on the road, and when he saw a tiny ant toiling by, he would step over it, so as not to harm it. The Tin Woodman knew very well he had no heart, and therefore he took great care never to be cruel or unkind to anything.

"You people with hearts," he said, "have something to guide you, and need never do wrong. But I have no heart, and so I must be very careful. When Oz gives me a heart, of course, I needn't mind so much."

They were obliged to camp out that night under a large tree in the forest, for there were no houses near. The tree made a good, thick covering to protect them from the dew, and the Tin Woodman chopped a great pile of wood with his axe, and Dorothy built a splendid fire that warmed her and made her feel less lonely. She and Toto ate the last of their bread, and now she did not know what they would do for breakfast.

"If you wish," said the Lion, "I will go into the forest and kill a deer for you. You can roast it by the fire, since your tastes are so peculiar that you prefer cooked food, and then you will have a very good breakfast."

"Don't! Please don't," begged the Tin Woodman. "I should certainly weep if you killed a poor deer, and then my jaws would rust again."

But the Lion went away into the forest and found his own supper, and no one ever knew what it was, for he didn't mention it. And the Scarecrow found a tree full of nuts and filled Dorothy's basket with them, so that she would not be

241

hungry for a long time. She thought this was very kind and thoughtful of the Scarecrow, but she laughed heartily at the awkward way in which the poor creature picked up the nuts. His padded hands were so clumsy and the nuts were so small that he dropped almost as many as he put in the basket. But the Scarecrow did not mind how long it took him to fill the basket, for it enabled him to keep away from the fire, as he feared a spark might get into his straw and burn him up. So he kept a good distance away from the flames, and only came near to cover Dorothy with dry leaves when she lay down to sleep. These kept her very snug and warm, and she slept soundly until morning.

Unit Six
Changes

Remembering Last Summer

I used to have this terrific old dog named Pepper. He
wasn't any particular kind of dog, but he was one of the
best friends I ever had. My other really good friend was
Bobby Nelson. He lived next door. We built a great fort in
a tree that had been hit by lightning and had fallen over
in his yard. Every afternoon we'd all sit on my back
steps, eating peanut butter on cheese crackers, and Bobby
and I would tell each other the dreams we'd had the
night before. Sometimes our dreams were so exciting
we'd have to jump up and act them out. Then Pepper
would jump up, too, and run around and bark as if he'd
had the very same dream.

My grandma liked to sit in her rocker on the back
porch and listen to us while she worked on her knitting.
Grandma lives at our house. She doesn't look like the
grandmothers in books, but she's really a neat person.
She spends most of her time reading, taking care of her
plants, and knitting. I must have a jillion sweaters.

One time she asked me if she should make a sweater
for Pepper. I told her no, he wasn't that kind of a dog. I
realized afterwards that she was just kidding me. She
understood Pepper, and she knew he'd be embarrassed to
run around the neighborhood in a sweater. Instead she
made him a rug out of old scraps of material. We put it
in front of the kitchen radiator, and that was where
Pepper always slept.

"He is old like me," Grandma used to say. "I expect the heat feels good to his old bones on chilly mornings."

Anyway, one of my favorite remembering things is those lazy days of sitting on the back steps, sharing dreams and listening to the click-click-click of Grandma's knitting needles. One time Grandma even told us her dream. She dreamed our house didn't have any doors, and the only way she could get in it was to climb up this gigantic ladder and slide down a wiggly slide that went through the picture window. That's the neat kind of person my grandma is.

Then one day last summer, Bobby called me on the tin-can telephone we'd hooked up between our bedrooms. He yelled, "My father's got a new job. We're moving to Ohio."

That made me very mad at Bobby, even though I knew it wasn't his fault. I kept picturing him telling someone else his dreams or maybe even telling someone my dreams! I don't know why, but it really made me mad.

The day that Bobby moved was awful. First a big van came, and the movers packed up everything except the suitcases and boxes the Nelsons put in their station wagon. The only things left in the house were the little dents in the living-room carpet where the furniture had been. When it was time to say good-bye, I gave Bobby my book on insects, which he was always borrowing, and he gave me two of his Indian arrowheads.

Pepper and I watched the Nelsons drive off. Then we went and sat in the fort awhile and talked. Pepper was the best listener I ever met. I told him how upset I was and how I felt alone all of a sudden. He licked my nose a

couple of times to let me know he understood, but I could tell he wanted to do something more interesting. He hated for me to be sad. The fort was starting to feel kind of creepy anyway, so we went home.

After Bobby left, Pepper and I were together all the time. The people who moved in next door just had two grown-up boys, so there was no one else in the neighborhood to play with. One day a man came out with a chain saw and cut our fort up into little pieces and hauled it away, so Pepper and I started spending a lot of time down by the river. Sometimes I'd take my fishing pole and a can of worms, and sometimes we'd just look for turtles and wild flowers. On other days we'd stay home and help Grandma in the garden. Pepper liked cucumbers, and Grandma always gave him a fat juicy one if he was good and didn't dig.

247

Pepper even stayed with me when I practiced the piano. He would sit at my feet and make little growly sounds. He never cared too much for the piano except when I played "The Happy Farmer." Then he'd raise his head high and sing his heart out. He really liked that one, maybe because I had practiced it enough to get rid of most of the mistakes.

Then one terrible night, when we were catching lightning bugs, Pepper let out a cry and fell over. He just lay there shaking and trying to wag his tail a little. I ran and got Daddy, and right away he came back with me and carried Pepper into the house and laid him on his rug. I sat down next to Pepper and petted him and talked to him. He reached out and licked my hand, and then he just closed his eyes. Daddy reached down and felt Pepper's chest, and then he told me Pepper was dead. Daddy said his old heart had just stopped working.

"No, you're wrong!" I shouted. "You're wrong, wrong, wrong!"

I don't remember much more about that night, except that later Daddy wrapped Pepper up in his rug and carried him outside. I held the flashlight and knelt on the ground next to Pepper while Daddy dug a hole in the backyard. You know how your mouth feels after the dentist gives you a shot? Well, I felt like that all over, and I couldn't cry. I guess Mom put me to bed, because the next thing I knew, it was morning.

I lay in bed, pretending that the night before had just been the worst dream I'd ever had. Then I got up and tiptoed downstairs. No one else was awake yet. When I walked into the kitchen, Pepper's rug was gone. And when I went out to the backyard, there was the mound of lumpy dirt. I knew I couldn't pretend any more. I sat down on the back-porch steps and wished that Bobby still lived next door. I felt terrible.

Pretty soon I heard noises in the kitchen. Mom was up making coffee. I guess she knew how I felt, because for once she didn't make me eat breakfast. A little while later, Grandma came out and sat in her rocking chair. "Come and sit on my lap," she said to me.

"Oh, Grandma," I said. "I haven't sat on your lap in years. I'm way too big!"

"No, you're not," she said. "Come sit." I got on her lap, and she began rocking back and forth and humming a whispery tune. It was "The Happy Farmer." All of a sudden I started to cry, and Grandma kept humming and rocking while I cried and cried.

Finally I said, "Grandma, promise you'll never leave me."

"Oh, I can't promise that," she said. "Someday I'll have to leave you, just as Pepper did. Try not to be mad at me."

"I'd never be mad at you!" I told her.

"Oh, you just might," she said. "When Grandpa died, I got very angry at him."

"Why, Grandma?" I asked.

"For leaving me all alone. But I realized that Grandpa didn't want to leave me, and then I felt very sad."

"I'm so sad I don't think anything will be fun ever again," I said. "Did you ever stop feeling sad for Grandpa?"

"Yes, yes." She nodded. "I still miss Grandpa—I always will—but Grandpa didn't like me to be sad. He liked to see me laugh. 'Katherine,' he'd say, 'I love the

249

way you crinkle up your nose when you laugh.' " And she laughed softly, remembering Grandpa.

"He was right," I said. "Your nose does get crinkly when you laugh. I never noticed before."

I was starting to feel a little better. We didn't say anything for a while. Grandma just rocked me and hummed some more, and I thought about what she had said and about how Pepper had hated for me to be sad. He would always try to cheer me up by licking me in the face or by bringing me some dumb toy to play with.

Later that morning, Grandma and I took a walk down by the river. I showed her all the river things Pepper and I loved—the yellow wild flowers buzzing with honeybees, the lovely plunky frogs, and even the wishing rock. Grandma and I each took a turn making a wish, and then we skipped stones on the river.

"Grandma," I said. "You never told me you knew how to skip stones!" I was really sort of surprised, and I suddenly realized there were a lot of things I didn't know about her.

On the way home, Grandma discovered a tiny tree growing among the flowers. She told me to run home and get her gardening shovel. When I got back, we dug up the tree, being careful not to cut off the roots. I carried it home, and we planted it right in the lumps that Pepper was buried under. Then we watered it with Grandma's sprinkling can. Grandma said that in the spring, when our tree bloomed, we'd always remember Pepper. In a way he'd become a part of the tree.

The rest of that afternoon, Grandma and I sat on the back-porch steps and ate peanut butter on cheese crackers and talked. I bet she told me a hundred stories I'd never had time to listen to before.

That day I spent with Grandma after Pepper died was August twenty-first of last summer. And now it's spring already.

Today when I walked home from school, Grandma was watching for me at the picture window. "Come with me!" she said, as she came running out to meet me. "I could hardly wait for you to get here." I followed her out to the backyard, and she headed straight for our little tree. It had ten cottony white blossoms on it.

"Oh, the flowers are so pretty!" I said. "What kind of a tree is it?"

Grandma's nose got all crinkly. "Why, it's a dogwood tree, of course!" she said. Then we laughed, and I gave her a big hug. Grandma is one of the most terrific friends I've ever had.

The Fisherman Who Needed a Knife

MARIE WINN

Long, long ago, people did not use money. Instead, they traded with each other to get the things they needed.

What is trading?

When you say *"I'll* give you my dump truck if *you* give me your kite"—that's trading.

When you say *"I'll* give you my candy if *you* give me your ice cream"—that's trading.

Long, long ago, before people used money, everybody traded different things. A fisherman traded the fish he caught for the other things he needed. A baker traded bread. A hatmaker traded hats. A potter traded pots.

252

Once upon a time, long, long ago, a fisherman needed a sharp knife. Since there was no money long ago, he could not go out and buy one.

So he took one of his fish and wrapped it up to keep it fresh. He took the fish to the knifemaker's house.

"Here is a fresh fish I caught today," he said to the knifemaker. "I will give you the fish if you give me a sharp knife that I need."

"I would be glad to trade with you," said the knifemaker, "but this very morning someone brought me a large fish and traded it for a knife. Now I don't need another fish. What I need is a new hat. My old hat fell into the fire yesterday."

The fisherman took his fish and went to the hatmaker's house.

"Here is a fresh fish," he said to the hatmaker. "I will give you the fish if you give me a hat. Then I can give the hat to the knifemaker and trade it for a sharp knife that I need."

"Sorry," said the hatmaker. "I already have a nice fish for my supper. A girl brought it this morning and traded it for a cap. But I have no more bread in the house. What I need is a crusty loaf of bread."

The fisherman took his fish and went to the baker's house.

"Here is a fresh fish," he said to the baker. "I will give you the fish if you give me a crusty loaf of bread. Then I can give the bread to the hatmaker and trade it for a hat. Then I can take the hat to the knifemaker and trade it for a sharp knife that I need."

"I'm afraid I don't need any fish today," said the baker. "This morning my wife went fishing and she caught an enormous fish. But my best pot has a crack in it. What I need is a new pot."

Once more the fisherman went off with his fish. He went
to the potter's house.

"Here is a fresh fish," he said to the potter. "I will give
you the fish if you give me a pot. Then I can give the pot to
the baker and trade it for a loaf of bread. Then I can take the
bread to the hatmaker and trade it for a hat. And then I can
give the hat to the knifemaker and trade it for a sharp knife
that I need."

The potter looked at the fish. She sniffed it with her nose.
She picked it up to feel how heavy it was.

"This is a good fish," she said. "It would make a
delicious supper, fried over the fire. I will be happy to trade
you a pot for this fine fish."

The fisherman gave the fish to the potter and traded it for a strong, round pot.

The fisherman took the pot to the baker and traded it for a crusty loaf of bread.

Then, he took the bread to the hatmaker and traded it for a soft leather hat.

At last the fisherman took the hat and went to the knifemaker's house.

He said to the knifemaker, "First I traded my fish for a pot. Then I traded the pot for a loaf of bread. Then I traded the bread for this hat. And now I would like to trade this hat for a sharp knife that I need."

The knifemaker took the hat and tried it on. It fit very well and kept the sun out of her eyes. She picked out a knife she had made and gave it to the fisherman.

"Here is my best, sharpest knife," said the knifemaker. "But what a lot of trouble you had getting this knife. You had to make so many trades! You had to go to so many people before you found someone who needed your fish!"

"Yes," said the fisherman, "everybody needs *something*, but it's not always a fish that they need."

"I have the same trouble," said the knifemaker. "Sometimes I have to make many trades before I get the things I need. Sometimes trading takes so much time that I hardly have time left to make knives."

The fisherman thought very hard and then he had an idea.

"Wouldn't it be good if there were some easier way for us to get the things we need?" he asked. "Instead of everybody trading different things—fish and pots and bread and knives—wouldn't it be easier if people used one special thing for trading?"

"What kind of special thing could people use?" asked the knifemaker.

"It would have to be something really special, something you couldn't find just anywhere. Otherwise people would not need to work to get it.

"It might be special, colored seashells, or little bits of gold or silver or copper. It might be almost anything, just so long as everyone used the same special thing," said the fisherman.

"That is a fine idea," said the knifemaker. "That is a great idea! We wouldn't have to do all that trading."

"If you gave me some pieces of that special thing, you could get a knife right away. You wouldn't have to make all those trades. I could give some pieces of the special thing to the hatmaker and get a hat right away. I wouldn't have to wait until someone needed a knife to get a hat," said the knifemaker.

"That's it!" said the fisherman. "Everyone would get some pieces of that special thing for the work they do—for the fish they catch or the bread they bake or the pots or knives they make. And then everyone would use those pieces of that special thing to get the things they need—food or clothes or tools."

The fisherman and the knifemaker talked to all the people who lived and worked in their village. They told them their idea.

"A great idea," everybody agreed. "Why didn't we think of it before?"

They picked small pieces of metal to be their special thing for trading. Everybody used the same pieces of metal. And life was much easier and better for everyone.

Today too we use a special thing for getting what we need. Our special thing is also small pieces of metal —pennies, nickels and dimes, quarters and half-dollars. We also use specially decorated pieces of paper called dollars that we can trade anywhere for change—for pennies, nickels, dimes, quarters, and half-dollars. We call that special thing *money*.

Money is not good for anything by itself. You can't eat it like bread. You can't wear it like a hat. You can't cook in it like a pot. But it makes it easier for us to get the things we need.

Today a fisherman still catches fish, just as a fisherman did long ago. But a fisherman today sells his fish for money. Then, if he needs a knife, he can use that money to buy a knife.

He doesn't have to trade his fish for a pot, the pot for a loaf of bread, the loaf of bread for a hat, and the hat for a knife, the way a fisherman had to do long, long ago, before people used money.

257

Spells

I dance and dance without any feet—
This is the spell of the ripening wheat.

With never a tongue I've a tale to tell—
This is the meadow-grasses' spell.

I give you health without any fee—
This is the spell of the apple-tree.

I rhyme and riddle without any book—
This is the spell of the bubbling brook.

Without any legs I run for ever—
This is the spell of the mighty river.

I fall for ever and not at all—
This is the spell of the waterfall.

Without a voice I roar aloud—
This is the spell of the thunder-cloud.

No button or seam has my white coat—
This is the spell of the leaping goat.

I can cheat strangers with never a word—
This is the spell of the cuckoo-bird.

We have tongues in plenty but speak no names—
This is the spell of the fiery flames.

The creaking door has a spell to riddle—
I play a tune without any fiddle.

—James Reeves

258

Demeter and Persephone

HELEN WEBBER

The ancient Greeks told this story of Demeter and Persephone to explain the coming of winter and the return of spring.

In the valley of Enna in Sicily, near a lake in the woods, the ground is covered with flowers, and it is always spring. To this place came the lovely Persephone one day, to gather flowers with her young friends. She filled her basket with lilies and violets, and wandered off in search of daffodils.

It happened then that Hades, the lord of the underworld, where the spirits of the dead dwell, flew by in his golden chariot, drawn by enormous, coal-black horses. Hades saw the beautiful Persephone and at once fell in love with her. Without a word he seized her, swept her into his chariot, and carried her off.

Persephone cried out to her mother and her friends for help, but it was of no use. Hades urged his swift horses on. When they reached the River Cyane, he struck the riverbank with his three-pronged spear, and the earth opened and gave them passage to the underworld.

Now, Persephone was the only daughter of Demeter, goddess of the harvest, who looked after the farmers' crops and who first taught mortals to use the plow. Demeter had heard Persephone's echoing cry from afar, but when she reached the lake, she could find no trace of her daughter. She found only the wild flowers strewn where Persephone had dropped them.

259

Wrapping herself in a cloud, Demeter set out in search of Persephone. She went from one land to another, across the seas and rivers, all over the world. But she had no success and sadly returned at last to the banks of the River Cyane.

The spirit who lived in the river wanted to tell the sorrowing mother all she had seen, but dared not, for fear of Hades. So she took Persephone's sash, which she had found on the riverbank, and floated it to Demeter's feet.

When she saw Persephone's sash, Demeter understood that her child was underground. In her grief she blamed the innocent earth.

"Ungrateful earth," she cried, "which I have clothed with every green and growing thing! No more shall you enjoy my generosity."

Then she caused cattle to die and plows to break in the furrows. The grain failed to come up, and only thistles and brambles grew on the earth. Soon the lands of the earth were frozen and bare.

After seeing all this, the river nymph took courage and spoke. "Goddess, do not blame the earth. It opened against its will to give passage to your daughter. I can tell you of Persephone's fate, for I see her as I pass through the lower parts of the earth. She is the queen of the dark under-world—the prisoner and bride of the king of the dead. She grieves and eats nothing. She is sad, but not afraid."

After Demeter heard these things, she sped in her chariot toward Mount Olympus, where the gods dwelt. She knew that she needed powerful help to get her daughter back. She threw herself at the feet of Zeus, the king of the gods, and begged him to force Hades to give her daughter up.

Zeus knew that he must take the matter in hand, for he had heard the cries of misery from the people of the earth. He

knew that the poor earth would be icebound and lifeless as long as Demeter grieved for Persephone. "Very well," he said. "I shall command Hades to send Persephone back to you. But if she has tasted food in the underworld, then she must remain there. That is the law."

Then a messenger was sent from Zeus to the underworld. Hades was ordered to let Persephone return to her mother. At the messenger's words Persephone jumped up joyfully, eager to go. Hades scowled, for he knew that he must obey the word of Zeus and send his young bride back. But first he asked her to eat some pomegranate seeds. In her happiness Persephone ate four seeds.

When Zeus heard that Persephone had eaten the pomegranate seeds, he made a new judgment, for the people on earth could not remain in their misery. He sent for Demeter and said to her, "Because Persephone has tasted food in the underworld, she must henceforth spend a third part of every year there with her husband, Hades. For the rest of the year you will have your daughter to comfort you. Now be at peace. Send once again your good gifts to the earth."

Demeter accepted the judgment of Zeus with mixed joy and sorrow. Her beloved daughter was returned to her. Then she sent the sun and the rains to relieve the suffering earth.

So it was agreed, and so it has been ever since. For a third part of every year—one month for each seed she tasted —Persephone leaves her mother and goes down to the dark kingdom of the dead. During that time Demeter grieves and neglects the earth. Nothing grows. It is winter.

But at the end of four months Persephone returns to her mother. She brings joy to Demeter and fresh springtime to the earth.

The Snowflake

Before I melt,
Come, look at me!
This lovely icy filigree!
Of a great forest
In one night
I make a wilderness
Of white:
By skyey cold
Of crystals made,
All softly, on
Your finger laid,
I pause, that you
My beauty see:
Breathe, and I vanish
Instantly.

—Walter de la Mare

263

The Turn of the Year

LAURA INGALLS WILDER

The days were growing longer, but the cold was more intense. Father said:

> *"When the days begin to lengthen*
> *The cold begins to strengthen."*

At last the snow softened a little on the south and west slopes. At noon the icicles dripped. Sap was rising in the trees, and it was time to make sugar.

In the cold mornings just before sunrise, Almanzo and Father set out to the maple grove. Father had a big wooden yoke on his shoulders and Almanzo had a little yoke. From the ends of the yokes hung strips of moosewood bark, with large iron hooks on them, and a big wooden bucket swung from each hook.

In every maple tree Father had bored a small hole, and fitted a little wooden spout into it. Sweet maple sap was dripping from the spouts into small pails.

Going from tree to tree, Almanzo emptied the sap into his big buckets. The weight hung from his shoulders, but he steadied the buckets with his hands to keep them from swinging. When they were full, he went to the great caldron and emptied them into it.

The huge caldron hung from a pole set between two trees. Father kept a bonfire blazing under it, to boil the sap.

Almanzo loved trudging through the frozen wild woods. He walked on snow that had never been walked on before, and only his own tracks followed behind him. Busily he emptied the little pails into the buckets, and whenever he was thirsty he drank some of the thin, sweet, icy-cold sap.

He liked to go back to the roaring fire. He poked it and saw the sparks fly. He warmed his face and hands in the scorching heat and smelled the sap boiling. Then he went into the woods again.

At noon all the sap was boiling in the caldron. Father opened the lunch-pail, and Almanzo sat on the log beside him. They ate and talked. Their feet were stretched out to the fire, and a pile of logs was at their backs. All around them were snow and ice and wild woods, but they were snug and cosy.

265

After they had eaten, Father stayed by the fire to watch the sap, but Almanzo hunted wintergreen berries.

Under the snow on the south slopes the bright-red berries were ripe among their thick green leaves. Almanzo took off his mittens and pawed away the snow with his bare hands. He found the red clusters and filled his mouth full. The cold berries crunched between his teeth, gushing out their aromatic juice.

Nothing else was ever so good as wintergreen berries dug out of the snow.

Almanzo's clothes were covered with snow, his fingers were stiff and red with cold, but he never left a south slope until he had pawed it all over.

When the sun was low behind the maple-trunks, Father threw snow on the fire and it died in sizzles and steam. Then Father dipped the hot syrup into the buckets. He and Almanzo set their shoulders under the yokes again, and carried the buckets home.

They poured the syrup into Mother's big brass kettle on the cook-stove. Then Almanzo began the chores while Father fetched the rest of the syrup from the woods.

After supper, the syrup was ready to sugar off. Mother ladled it into six-quart milk-pans and left it to cool. In the morning every pan held a big cake of solid maple-sugar. Mother dumped out the round, golden-brown cakes and stored them on the top pantry shelves.

Day after day the sap was running, and every morning Almanzo went with Father to gather and boil it; every night Mother sugared it off. They made all the sugar they could use next year. Then the last boiling of syrup was not sugared off; it was stored in jugs down cellar, and that was the year's syrup.

266

When Alice came home from school she smelled Almanzo, and she cried out, "Oh, you've been eating wintergreen berries!"

She thought it wasn't fair that she had to go to school while Almanzo gathered sap and ate wintergreen berries. She said:

"Boys have all the fun."

She made Almanzo promise that he wouldn't touch the south slopes along Trout River, beyond the sheep pasture.

So on Saturdays they went together to paw over those slopes. When Almanzo found a red cluster he yelled, and when Alice found one she squealed, and sometimes they divided, and sometimes they didn't. But they went on their hands and knees all over those south slopes, and they ate wintergreen berries all afternoon.

Almanzo brought home a pailful of the thick, green leaves, and Alice crammed them into a big bottle. Mother filled the bottle with whisky and set it away. That was her wintergreen flavoring for cakes and cookies.

Every day the snow was melting a little. The cedars and spruces shook it off, and it fell in blobs from the bare branches of oaks and maples and beeches. All along the walls of barns and houses the snow was pitted with water falling from the icicles, and finally the icicles fell crashing.

The earth showed in wet, dark patches here and there. The patches spread. Only the trodden paths were still white, and a little snow remained on the north sides of buildings and woodpiles. Then the winter term of school ended and spring had come.

One morning Father drove to Malone. Before noon he

came hurrying home, and shouted the news from the buggy. The New York potato-buyers were in town!

Royal ran to help hitch the team to the wagon, Alice and Almanzo ran to get bushel baskets from the woodshed. They rolled them bumpity-bump down the cellar stairs, and began filling them with potatoes as fast as they could. They filled two baskets before Father drove the wagon to the kitchen porch.

Then the race began. Father and Royal hurried the baskets upstairs and dumped them into the wagon, and Almanzo and Alice hurried to fill more baskets faster than they were carried away.

Almanzo tried to fill more baskets than Alice, but he couldn't. She worked so fast that she was turning back to the bin while her hoopskirts were still whirling the other way. When she pushed back her curls, her hands left smudges on her cheeks. Almanzo laughed at her dirty face, and she laughed at him.

"Look at yourself in the glass! You're dirtier than I be!"

They kept the baskets full; Father and Royal never had to wait. When the wagon was full, Father drove away in a hurry.

It was mid-afternoon before he came back, but Royal and Almanzo and Alice filled the wagon again while he ate some cold dinner, and he hauled another load away. That night Alice helped Royal and Almanzo do the chores. Father was not there for supper; he did not come before bedtime. Royal sat up to wait for him. Late in the night Almanzo heard the wagon, and Royal went out to help Father curry and brush the tired horses who had done twenty miles of hauling that day.

The next morning, and the next, they all began
loading potatoes by candlelight, and Father was gone
with the first load before sunrise. On the third day the
potato-train left for New York city. But all Father's
potatoes were on it.

"Five hundred bushels at a dollar a bushel," he said
to Mother at supper. "I told you when potatoes were
cheap last fall that they'd be high in the spring."

That was five hundred dollars in the bank. They were
all proud of Father, who raised such good potatoes and
knew so well when to store them and when to sell them.

"That's pretty good," Mother said, beaming. They all
felt happy.

Voice of the Turtle

For, lo, the winter is past,
The rain is over and gone;
The flowers appear on the earth;
The time of the singing of birds is come,
And the voice of the turtle is heard in our land.

—The Bible

The Chippewa

CAROL ANN BALES

Long before white people came to this country from
Europe, the people of the Chippewa tribe lived near the
Upper Great Lakes. This land had been their home for
hundreds of years. The Chippewa had learned many things
about living on their land and about living together.

The first white people to reach the Great Lakes came
from France. They brought with them many things that the
Chippewa had never seen before. The Chippewa traded
beaver furs to the French in return for some of these new
things—metal traps for hunting, iron kettles, glass beads,
and guns. Some of the things that the French brought—
such as liquor and new diseases—were not good for the
Indians.

The Chippewa taught the white people many things.
They taught them how to live on the land and how to travel
through the wilderness.

More and more white settlers began to move into the
land of the Chippewa. The food of the Chippewa—deer,
moose, bear, and reindeer—became scarce. The demand
for beaver furs came to an end. The Chippewa no longer
had a way of buying the new things that they had come to
need.

271

Life became harder for the Chippewa. They were forced to live on reservations, which they were promised would be Indian land forever. White soldiers were sent to run the reservations, and some of them treated the Indians badly. Fights broke out, and in the end the Chippewa lost.

The reservations were small. The Chippewa had been hunters, but to live on the reservations they had to become farmers. They were not permitted to practice their religion. Chippewa children were sent away from their families to boarding schools. There they were forbidden to speak their own language and were taught the ways of white people.

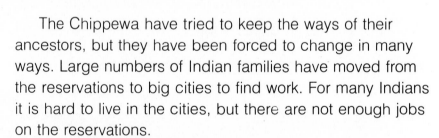

The Chippewa have tried to keep the ways of their ancestors, but they have been forced to change in many ways. Large numbers of Indian families have moved from the reservations to big cities to find work. For many Indians it is hard to live in the cities, but there are not enough jobs on the reservations.

When you read the next selection, you will see that Kevin Cloud is a lot like you. But you will also see, if you read carefully, that Kevin knows some things from a long time ago that have been passed down to him.

This makes him special. There are many such people in our country who have had special ideas passed down to them from their parents, grandparents, and great-grandparents. Perhaps you are one of them too.

Kevin Cloud

CAROL ANN BALES

My name is Kevin Wayne Cloud.

I was born on Thanksgiving Day in Cook County Hospital in Chicago. The first thing I did was to start flying around the room. Mama says she doubts that I flew, but I did.

I like to tease like that. I tease everybody. Sometimes when I tease Mama, she pretends to beat me up. I like that.

I'm ten, but I've already got a lot of scars. Mama calls them my growing-up scars. Once I fell when I was a baby. Another time a kid threw a bottle at me, and last year a kid at school pushed me against a desk.

I'm an Indian, an American Indian. My family belongs to the Chippewa tribe. We live in the city. I've got two older sisters, Sheila and Brenda, and a little brother, Mark. Then there's Dino, our dog. And Joey, our cat—and Mama. My uncle Obe lives with us too, and Grandma.

Grandma speaks Indian. Mama does too, and all my aunts and uncles. I understand a few words. Grandma tries to teach us.

Grandma is always going to powwows. I go once in a while. When we went to a powwow last summer, Grandma wore a Chippewa dress that she made. She has five Indian dresses. Three are Chippewa with beadwork. The other two have ribbons. A Winnebago lady made them. Winnebagos are a different tribe.

I wore some Indian moccasins from Cass Lake in Minnesota and danced the rabbit dance. Grandma helped cook and serve. The Indian food we had was fry bread and hominy. But I liked the fried chicken best. That's one of my favorite foods.

It was cold that night, and they started a big fire that we could sit around to keep warm. They danced for a long time. Grandma said it was a real good powwow that night.

Last summer we went up to the reservation in Minnesota to harvest wild rice and to visit Aunt Rose. She's Mama's cousin. It was a long way. I kept asking how much further it was.

There are many birch trees on the path to the place on the lake where Aunt Rose launched her boat. Grandma says the place was an old Indian campsite and that not everybody knows about it. She says she remembers when they used to camp there before white people harvested wild rice or made rules about it.

The old Chippewa used the bark from the white birch trees to make canoes, to cover their wigwams, and for rice trays and sugar baskets. They knew how to strip the bark without killing the trees. Grandma says she used to watch my great-grandfather making canoes. She says everybody who knew how to make them is probably dead, and besides, it's hard to get the wood. That's why they don't make them now.

It rained the first day of ricing. But Aunt Rose said that that wouldn't make any difference. Everybody got up early. We saw many cars with boats on top. Each time a car went by, Grandma said, "There goes an Indian to rice." Only people who live on the reservation are allowed to rice.

Most people don't have their own boats. Aunt Rose rented hers. She bought a license and a pair of knockers. Knockers are long wooden sticks that are used to knock the rice into the boat.

Aunt Rose dropped some tobacco in the water before she started ricing. Mama says that's the old Chippewa way of giving thanks for the rice. The old religion is called Midewiwin.

Aunt Rose lives in a house in the town of Cass Lake. My cousin and me, we had a dirt fight there. That was fun. Before we left, Mama bought some wild rice at the store. We usually have white rice at home. Mama says the wild rice you buy in Chicago doesn't taste right, and it costs too much money.

We were all tired when we got back, but it was a good trip.

Inventions
That Changed the World

DAVID C. COOKE

Of all the abilities possessed by humans, perhaps the most important is imagination. This one ability makes humans different from all the other creatures in the animal kingdom.

Ever since people first walked the earth, they have been forced to put their imaginations to work. It was too difficult to drag heavy objects, and so they invented the wheel. They were weaker than many other animals, and so they invented the spear and the bow and arrow. They could not run rapidly or carry heavy loads, so they tamed horses and other animals to work for them.

Imagination has been the great force behind every invention from toothpicks to television, from matches to motion pictures, from nails to nylon, from anchors to atomic energy.

According to the dictionary, the word *invent* means "to create or devise in the imagination." Very simply, this means to think of something that is needed, or to think of a better way to do something.

The machines discussed in this article were all invented in the 1700s. They brought great changes in the way goods were manufactured, and so marked the beginning of the Industrial Revolution.

Steam Engine

The first known steam engine was invented by Hero in ancient Greece around the year 120 B.C. Hero called his device an *aeolipile*, naming it after Aeolus, the god of the winds. The *aeolipile* was a kind of steam engine, but it was never considered anything more than a strange but wonderful toy.

Others after Hero tried to use the power of steam to perform various types of work. Some of their machines were very strange. One of them, a metal figure of a man, blew steam to turn a paddle wheel. This wheel in turn

278

made weights go up and down to pound various powders into medicines. Steam power continued to be a strange toy with little practical use.

Then about the year 1690 Dionysius Papin of France invented the first steam engine to have a cylinder and piston. When Papin forced steam into the bottom of the cylinder, the piston was pushed upward by the pressure. After the steam cooled in the cylinder, the piston came down again. Papin had the right idea, but he didn't know what to do with it.

Thomas Newcomen, an English blacksmith, was the first person to really put steam to work. Using Papin's cylinder-and-piston idea, he made an engine that would pump water from great depths. This machine saved the coal industry in England. However, Newcomen did not know how to cool the steam quickly enough. His engine could make only twelve or fifteen strokes per minute, which was very slow.

Then one day James Watt, a Scottish machinist, was called in to repair a Newcomen engine. Watt recognized the basic problem and set about to improve the engine. He experimented for several years and finally hit upon an idea. If steam could be used to force the piston up, why not force it down again with more steam from the other side? The used steam could be let out through an automatic valve.

Watt had his first engine ready in 1765, and it worked exactly as he had expected it would. This was the beginning of a new way of life. The world finally had mechanical power to turn the wheels of industry.

Spinning and Weaving Machinery

As recently as only 200 years ago, producing things people needed was slow and difficult in even the most advanced countries. There were no factories as we know them today, and everything had to be made by hand.

Clothing was especially difficult to make in those days, for all thread had to be spun by hand and all cloth woven by hand-operated machines. This was a very slow and tiring process.

Then, about 1732, an English weaver named John Kay got an idea for a method to throw the shuttle back and forth in his loom by pulling on a cord. He called his invention the fly shuttle. With it he was able to weave much more cloth in a day than ever before.

However, this invention was not enough, for the process of spinning thread was still painfully slow. The first person to come up with a better system was James Hargreaves. In 1767 he made a machine that, by turning a crank, would spin up to eight strands of thread at the same time. He called his device the spinning jenny.

Two years later Richard Arkwright improved the Hargreaves invention and powered it by a water wheel. He called his spinning machine the water frame. In 1775 Samuel Crompton combined the best features of the spinning jenny and the water frame into his much better "mule," which made the finest thread that anyone had ever seen and also made it much faster.

Suddenly there was a plentiful supply of thread, but weaving was still too slow. An Englishman named Edmund Cartwright began to study weaving machines, watching people work them for hours on end. He came to the conclusion that weaving could be done automatically by machine. Cartwright set about designing such a machine.

He had his first loom ready in 1787. It was turned by a crank. A short time later he added a steam engine for power. This was the true beginning of the Industrial Revolution. Mechanization had begun, and all because material was needed to make clothes for the people of England.

Cotton Gin

We now consider cotton to be one of nature's greatest gifts. However, it was once considered something close to a curse, because a long, tiring process was necessary to remove seeds from the raw cotton fibers. For centuries this was done by hand. Even the fastest workers could pluck seeds from only a few pounds of cotton in a working day, which often extended from sunrise to sunset.

In the early years of the United States there were so few people that cotton farmers could not hire enough people to work their farms. The farmers also wanted to cultivate more land so that they could meet the huge demands of the British textile industry.

In 1792 Eli Whitney, of Massachusetts, went to Georgia, where he spent several months on a cotton plantation. This was the first time he had seen how cotton was grown and picked and how the seeds were removed. He thought it should be possible to develop a machine that could separate the seeds from the cotton without harming the fibers. The following year he built his first cotton gin, which was to become one of the most important factors in the creation of America's large cotton industry.

Whitney's machine consisted of a cylinder to which a number of sawlike teeth were attached. When the cylinder revolved, the teeth passed through a fixed comb. As cotton was fed into the machine, the teeth pulled the fibers through and the seeds were left behind. The much larger mechanical cotton gins of today still operate on this same principle, but they are much faster.

The cotton gin enabled cotton planters to supply textile manufacturers with the raw material they needed. The Industrial Revolution was now in full swing.

Unit Seven
Achievements

A Trip Through the Night

HOLLING C. HOLLING

In the winter, Grandmother Mink Woman often took
Flying Squirrel fishing through the ice. Many a pickerel,
bass, and bluegill came to the end of its swimming on
the bone point of their spear, and fresh fish was on hand
whenever anyone was hungry for it.

When early spring came with a rush and sap crept up
the trunks of trees, a great party from the village went
into the maple forests for sugar. For days they boiled the
sap down to a thick syrup. Then they left it to harden in

284

empty clamshells and wooden bowls. Two weeks of this stored up thousands of cakes of maple sugar, enough for a year.

After that came frogs singing again in the marshes, and blossoms and new leaves. Mink Woman dug herbs and secret medicines and taught Flying Squirrel many things about roots and leaves.

"You were named Flying Squirrel," said Mink Woman one evening, "because that animal has good eyes and knows its way about the woods in the dark. Did you know that?"

"Yes, Grandmother, and I think that the magic of my totem animal has crept into me, for I see in the woods very well after dark. I can even find my way perfectly in new country, in the darkest night when there are no stars. I've done it often, berry picking and wandering in the forest."

"Ah," said Mink Woman, "that little squirrel has given you good medicine. The day may come when it will serve you well."

One afternoon Mink Woman decided to make a new bulrush mat for her sleeping platform. She always liked to weave her mats in the early morning while the dew was on everything.

"Dew keeps the rushes supple," she explained. "Wetting them with water doesn't do the same thing at all. They should be picked in the evening and woven in the morning. So, Flying Squirrel, you get me some new rushes. Go over to Rush Lake, where they are thick. And remember that I want the rushes by my door before the dew is off tomorrow morning. It should not take you long to get them."

285

Flying Squirrel had a small canoe that she always used. It had blunt ends and would not tip easily. It was a quarter-mile paddle on the big lake to a creek that flowed for a little way through a marshy place and emptied into Rush Lake. The girl reached Rush Lake just at twilight, but the dusk did not hamper her work. She lay down in the bow of the canoe and snapped the stems of the bulrushes off at the water line, piling them behind her. Every time she pulled on the rushes, her canoe slid forward, and she gradually made a path through the thick growth.

Darkness came down quickly. Loons called. Ducks whipped through the reeds, squawking, and went over with a whir of wings. She could hear a loud splashing from time to time and knew that a cow moose was feeding on lily pads in the shallow lake with a calf beside her. It grew so dark she could scarcely see the other end of the canoe, but she knew what was going on all about her in the night.

Then she heard a different sort of splash, toward the creek. To you or me it might have been made by a moose or a deer or by a fish leaping. But that splash set Flying Squirrel all a-tingle. She stopped her work and, by pulling on rushes, worked her way cautiously toward the entrance of the creek. What was that shadow on the shore, a little blacker than the trees? It came down to the creek, crouching. It was no wild animal!

And then, clear and long, Flying Squirrel heard the call of the great horned owl. But just as she knew the shadow was no wild animal, the girl knew that the call was not made by an owl. The hair on her head rose, and a creeping sensation went along her spine.

She tried to be calm. Perhaps it was some of the village boys playing tricks on her. She edged the canoe in toward the shore and crept out on a log. By inching along on her hands and knees over grass and pine needles, she came to the creek. And there she saw a man.

He was standing by a tree, his back to her. She could see his body against the gray clouds in the sky. In his hands were arrows and a bow. Even as she watched, his head went back, and he gave the call of the owl, "Who-whoo! Whooo! Whoooo!"

Flying Squirrel had seen enough. This was a scout, calling in the advance guards of a war party. She knew what it meant. Enemies were collecting to raid her own village. But she did not lose her head. It was night. She had not been discovered. She could not paddle back through the creek, but she could paddle to the other side of Rush Lake and go on foot over the three hills that separated it from the village. She inched her way back to the place where she had left the canoe.

But the canoe was gone! Leaning far over, she saw a moccasin track on the muddy shore. Then she heard a whispered voice in the brush, another answering. She crawled out on the log and let herself down gently into the water. It crept up and up, a cold ring enclosing her body, until it touched her chin. She felt sure that she had made no ripple. She found a small, floating stump, and ducking under, came up on the other side.

Zip, thug! She had been seen or heard, after all! She did not stir. Again she heard, zip, thug! The stump heeled over a little. Against the sky she saw two arrows, still quivering, embedded in the wood. She heard a soft step on the bank, then the two voices again. Two warriors were joking with each other about shooting at a log. Then the voices went away.

She knew that she must hurry to work her way across the lake and over the three hills. Pulling on rushes, she went forward, still behind the stump. But the tops of the rushes waved as she pulled, and she was afraid the men would see the motion. Then she found the trail of plucked rushes she had made. She could pull on the stubs and never show a movement.

As she went past the creek opening, inch by inch, she saw shadows leaping. The men were crossing the creek. Would they leave someone behind to look for the owner of the canoe? She could not do anything but keep going.

It seemed hours before her feet touched a mucky shore, and she pulled her body out into the thick cedar branches. All her Flying Squirrel medicine must come to her aid now. She worked swiftly up one hill, over logs and through thickets, led on safely by the strange power she had described to Mink Woman. The second hill was worse than the first, but she crossed it. She judged it was about midnight when she cautiously came down the slope of the third hill and saw an opening in the forest wall. The cornfields! But what was that behind that cornhill? An enemy warrior, lying full length between the rows! They had beat her to the village.

However, she knew a little crooked path, and she followed it among squash vines and pumpkins. No arrows came. Off there in the dark was a wickiup. Could she make it? She came to a pile of wood, and that gave her an idea. Why couldn't she pretend to be a girl sent out for more wood? She knew the men would not attack until early morning. Surely they would not kill her now

and have the whole village warned. So she filled her arms with wood. And then, yawning and dropping a stick now and then, she walked directly toward the wickiup.

On the way she met a sentry of the village guard, who had no more idea than a chipmunk that enemies were in his territory. Flying Squirrel whispered the news to him, and without making any reply, he walked quietly to the nearest wickiup. In the dark, word was passed from wickiup to wickiup until the whole camp was warned. With no noise, warriors armed themselves, while women and children crept out of bed and hid under the platforms. They piled baskets and bundles behind them for protection against arrows.

When Flying Squirrel reached her wickiup, she told everything to her father and Mink Woman. Granny folded the girl in her arms and made her a cozy bed under the platform. But tired as she was, for a long time Flying Squirrel could not sleep.

All those enemy warriors strung about the camp! What a battle there would be! Finally she did sleep a little, but she was awakened by a hoot from that imitation owl. Through the door she could see the gray of early morning. Would they come now?

A shrill war whoop split the air, then another, and another. There were calls and yells, and the whole village seemed to be turned upside down. She heard arrows thud into the bark roof. One came through, dangling by its feathers just above her head. But the men of the village were shooting back, and soon the war whoops of the enemy changed to cries of fear.

Flying Squirrel could not stand it any longer. She ran out and saw that the village was ringed by her own people. The enemy were dropping right and left. When the sun came up, she saw what had happened. The enemy, instead of taking the village by surprise, had been taken by surprise themselves. Those who were alive had taken to the woods, with angry warriors from the village after them.

291

Around the fires for generations after, they told the story of Flying Squirrel and her trip through the night. The village had lost five men, it is true, but those men had died fighting bravely. Out of the sixty enemy warriors, only seven had got away. The whole tribe gave a great feast in Flying Squirrel's honor, and the dancing went on for days and days. The village was in peace, after that, for many summers.

John Henry

American Folk Song

When John Henry was a little baby,
Sitting on his mammy's knee,
He took a piece of steel in his right hand,
Said, steel will be the death of me,
O Lord, steel will be the death of me.

John Henry drove steel on the Southern,
Drove it on the CB and Q,
On the old Rock Island and the Santa Fe,
Baltimore Ohio too, O Lord,
Baltimore Ohio too.

John Henry had a hammer,
Weighed nearly forty pound,
Every time John made a strike,
He saw his steel go two inches down,
O Lord, saw his steel go two inches down.

Now the captain said to John Henry,
I'm going to bring my steam drill around.
John Henry said, I'd rather be dead,
Than let a steam drill beat me down,
O Lord, let a steam drill beat me down.

The man that invented the steam drill,
He thought he was mighty fine.
John Henry sank the steel fourteen feet
While the steam drill made only nine,
O Lord, while the steam drill made only nine.

John Henry was hammering on the mountain,
His hammer was striking fire.
He hammered so hard that he broke his poor heart,
He laid down his hammer and he died,
O Lord, he laid down his hammer and he died.

John Henry, O John Henry!
Sing it if you can—
High and low and everywhere you go,
He died with his hammer in his hand,
O Lord, he died with his hammer in his hand.

The Fox and the Cat

AESOP

A fox was boasting to a cat of all the clever ways it had to escape from its enemies. "I have a whole bag of tricks," the fox said, "which contains a hundred ways of escaping my enemies."

"I have only one," said the cat, "but I can generally manage with that."

Just at that moment they heard the cry of a pack of hounds coming towards them. The cat immediately scampered up a tree and hid in the boughs. "This is my plan," called the cat. "What are you going to do?"

The fox thought first of one way, then of another, and while it was trying to decide, the hounds came nearer and nearer. At last the fox, still undecided, was caught by the hounds and killed by the hunters.

The cat, who had been looking on, said, *"Better one safe way than a hundred on which you cannot depend."*

295

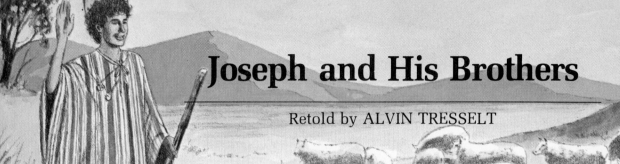

Joseph and His Brothers

Retold by ALVIN TRESSELT

There was once a boy named Joseph, the beloved son of
his father, Jacob. His ten older brothers were jealous
when they saw their father favor Joseph, and they could
not say a good word for the boy.

Now Jacob was troubled by all this. But he loved his
son greatly and gave him a coat of many colors to show
his love. And the brothers hated Joseph in their hearts.

One night Joseph had a dream, and when he told it to
his brothers, they hated him more. "I dreamed we were
binding sheaves of grain in the field," he said. "My sheaf
stood upright, and your sheaves gathered around mine
and bowed down to it."

Then Joseph had still another dream, and he told his
father and brothers, "I dreamed that the sun and moon
and eleven stars bowed down to me."

Jacob scolded him, saying, "What is this dream? Shall
I and your mother and your brothers indeed come to bow
down to you?" And Joseph's ten older brothers envied
him all the more.

One day the brothers were in a far-off place, tending
their father's sheep. Jacob, wishing to know if all was
well, sent Joseph to find them. When the brothers saw

Joseph approach, wearing his many-colored coat, they plotted to kill him and cast him into a pit. Then on their return to their father's tents, they would tell Jacob that a wild beast had killed his son.

But Reuben spoke up and said, "Let us not have his blood on our hands. We will cast him into a pit to live or die as it might be."

And when Joseph approached them, they seized him and stripped him of his coat and threw him into a pit in the wilderness. At that moment they spied a caravan of

297

Ishmaelites with their camels, carrying spices to Egypt. One of the brothers said, "Let us not leave Joseph in the pit, but sell him as a slave to the traders so that he will be carried out of the land of Canaan."

And so it was. The brothers sold Joseph for twenty pieces of silver, and they took his coat and dipped it in the blood of a newly killed goat to show their father that Joseph had been slain by wild beasts. And Jacob was bowed with grief.

When the caravan arrived in Egypt, the traders sold Joseph to a man named Potiphar, the captain of Pharaoh's guard, and he served him well. Potiphar was pleased with Joseph, and he put him in charge of his fields and his house. But in time Joseph was unjustly accused of a crime, and he was thrown into prison.

Now it happened that the head butler and the head baker of the Pharaoh of Egypt had offended him, and they were also in the prison. One night each of the men had a strange dream. The butler said to Joseph, "I dreamed there was a vine with three branches that put forth blossoms, and the blossoms became three clusters of ripe grapes. These grapes did I press into Pharaoh's cup, and I gave it into his hand."

Joseph answered, saying that the three branches were three days and that after three days the butler would once more be serving Pharaoh his wine as he had done before.

Then the baker said, "I dreamed I had three white baskets on my head filled with cakes for Pharaoh, and the birds came and ate the cakes out of the top basket."

Joseph replied that the three baskets were three days and that after three days Pharaoh would have him hanged from a tree.

And so it was. In three days the butler was called back to the palace, but the baker was hanged. And Joseph spoke to the butler, saying, "Remember me when you speak to Pharaoh, for I am unjustly held in this prison." But the butler forgot Joseph.

When Joseph had been in prison for two years, Pharaoh had two dreams, and all the wise men of Egypt could not explain them. Then the butler remembered Joseph, and he said to Pharaoh, "There is in your prison a young man who has been unjustly accused of a crime. He has the power to interpret dreams."

Pharaoh sent for Joseph at once and told him his dreams. "I dreamed that seven fat cows came up out of the river Nile and fed in the reed grass. Then seven lean and hungry cows came up out of the river and they ate the seven fat cows. Then I slept and dreamed a second time. Seven good ears of corn grew upon one stalk. Then seven lean ears sprang up beside them. And the seven lean ears ate up the seven fat ears."

Joseph answered Pharaoh, saying, "The seven fat cows and the seven good ears are seven years of plenty. The seven lean cows and the seven lean ears are seven years of famine, when no food will grow in all the land. Therefore, let Pharaoh appoint someone to gather the grain for seven years and store it away so that when the years of famine come, there will be food."

And Pharaoh said to Joseph, "Since you have the power to read my dream, I will make you overseer of the land, second in power only to me. You will gather the grain for seven years against the days of famine that will follow."

And it was as Joseph had said. For seven years the crops were plentiful, and he gathered grain. Then the seven years of plenty came to an end and the seven years of famine began. There was famine in all lands, even in the land of Canaan where Jacob and his sons lived.

Now Jacob heard that there was grain in Egypt, and he sent ten of his sons there to buy grain. But Benjamin, the youngest, he kept by his side.

When the brothers came before Joseph, he knew them, but they knew him not. Joseph spoke roughly to them, saying, "You are spies who have come from the land of Canaan to see the weakness of Egypt in its time of famine." But the brothers protested and said they were the sons of Jacob, who was at home with their youngest brother, Benjamin, and had come only to buy food. They bowed before him and begged him to believe them. Then Joseph remembered his dream, and he hid his head and wept.

At last Joseph gave in, and he sent his brothers back to Canaan, commanding his steward to fill their sacks with grain and to return their money in the sacks. But he held his brother Simeon in Egypt, saying that when they returned for grain, they must bring Benjamin and that he would then free Simeon.

The brothers journeyed back to the land of Canaan, and when they opened the sacks, there was their money. They told their father all that had happened, and they were afraid in their hearts. Jacob answered them, saying, "You have taken my children from me. Joseph is dead, Simeon is in Egypt, and now you would have Benjamin."

The famine continued, and at last the day came when the grain was gone. Once more Jacob said to his sons, "Go again to Egypt and buy us a little food."

When they reminded their father that Benjamin must go with them in order to win the release of Simeon, his heart was heavy, but the need for food was very great. "Take with you gifts for the Egyptian," he said. "Take also double your money and your brother Benjamin. And may all my sons be returned to me."

When the brothers once more stood before Joseph, he still did not reveal himself to them. He set a great feast before them, showing special favor to his brother Benjamin. But when the feast was finished and the donkeys loaded with grain, Joseph secretly ordered that his own silver cup should be put in the sack of grain belonging to Benjamin. As soon as it was light, the men set forth, but soon the head steward rode up to them and said, "One of you has stolen my master's silver cup, and he demands that the thief become his slave."

The sacks were opened up in order, beginning with the eldest brother, and when the sack of Benjamin, the youngest, was opened, there was the cup. The brothers returned to Joseph's house and fell before him, begging for mercy, saying their father would surely die if they returned without their youngest brother.

Now at last did Joseph weep before his brothers. He embraced them and said, "I am he whom you sold into slavery. But be not grieved, for I was sent before you so that in the time of famine I would be here to preserve you and our people."

And Joseph forgave his brothers. He commanded that his father and all his family be brought to live in Egypt so that they might have food for all their days.

Penny Savings Bank

RUTH MORRIS GRAHAM

A kerosene lamp glowed on the kitchen table of a
Richmond, Virginia, house in 1910. A woman sat at the
table with a pair of scissors in one hand and a sheet of
cardboard in the other. The only sound was the soft creak
that scissors make when they do what they are supposed
to do.

"No, that's not right," the woman said to herself.

"What's not right, Mamma?" asked an eight-year-old
boy as he came through the door. "Are you cutting out
paper dolls?"

"Well, not quite. I'm trying to make a doll house, or
rather, a doll bank. Look at this, Melvin."

Maggie Lena Walker drew her son to her and showed him the lines she had drawn. Some, she said, were for cutting, and some were for folding.

"My mistake was that I was cutting a fold line. Now see, if we fold this up here, and bring that over here, these two edges will come together for pasting."

"Let me help," Melvin said. He opened the jar of paste, and, trying to do as his mother told him, he smeared the edges in the right places.

"Oh, it's a house!" he exclaimed when his mother finished assembling the little cardboard building.

"Right. Now we'll put some words on it." Mrs. Walker picked up her pencil and began to write large letters. P—E—N—N—

"I see," said Melvin. "It's a little Penny Savings Bank, just like the big bank you own on Clay Street."

Mrs. Walker nodded and finished her printing. "And here on top is the slot where pennies can be dropped in," she said. "I hope this will help children learn to save."

Melvin did not understand. A penny was such a little bit of money, and all around him he heard adults talk about dollars.

"But why should children save pennies?" he asked.

"Saving is important," his mother said. "It's more important for poor people than for rich ones. You know, we would not have the bank if a lot of poor people hadn't saved, and most of us started by saving pennies."

"But you're rich, Mamma. You never had to save pennies."

"Melvin, when I was your age, I was very poor. My parents were poor."

"Were you a slave?" the boy asked.

305

"No, but your grandmother and grandfather were. I was born *after* the Civil War. Still, my parents had never been to school. They couldn't earn much money. Then my father died, and my mother worked to raise her children and send us to school. That was when she taught us about saving, for whenever she had work, she always saved for the time when she might not. She had to save, mostly one and two pennies at a time, to get enough to buy us clothes and to pay her bills."

Melvin looked at his mother with wide eyes. "I'm glad you're not poor now, Mamma," he said.

Maggie Lena Walker was also glad that she no longer was poor, but she did not feel that she was rich. Nor did she feel that she no longer had work to do. She knew that many black people were very poor and needed to learn how to save money. And with her Penny Savings Bank models, she felt she could teach them.

The next day she took her sample bank to a printer and ordered five thousand sheets of cardboard with lines and letters like those on the sample.

The following week she started her rounds of schools. The teachers knew that she had founded the St. Luke Penny Savings Bank in 1903, and they were glad to have her talk to the boys and girls.

In each class Mrs. Walker talked about the bank. She told how it had opened with just the combined savings of a few people, how it had grown as other people put in their money. In her bank a person could start a new savings account with just one dollar.

"The many small savings accounts, added together, give the bank a large total of money," Mrs. Walker explained. "From the large total the bank makes loans to people so that they can buy homes, start small businesses, or send their children away to school."

She went to the chalkboard and wrote some figures. "To make things simple, let us say that 100 savers have on deposit $10 each; this means that the bank holds 100 times $10, which equals $1,000. Suppose the bank lends $500 to a family to buy a house, $300 to a man who wants to improve his business, and $200 to a couple who want to send their son to college. All the money saved by depositors in the bank will be helping these people. Do you understand that much?"

The students seemed to understand, but one boy was waving his hand. The teacher nodded to him.

"Suppose," the boy said, "that some of those depositors want to get their money back. What happens then?"

Mrs. Walker smiled. "That's a good question. Very simply, while this amount of money is being loaned out, other money is coming in. Some people are making deposits, and some people are paying back their loans. A bank never lets all its money out on loans."

Next a girl asked, "Who pays the bankers and the other people who do the work?"

"That comes from interest," Mrs. Walker said. "You see, the people who borrow money from the bank must pay interest; that is, they must pay back a little more than they borrowed. The interest is like profit for the bank. The profit from interest and from other activities enables the bank to pay its expenses and to grow."

After answering many other questions, Mrs. Walker showed the class her model of the St. Luke Penny Savings Bank. She gave the teacher enough printed cardboard for each student to cut and fold and paste a savings bank to take home. The teacher promised that as the boys and girls saved a dollar, the money would be sent to the real Penny Savings Bank so that an account could be opened in the name of the young saver.

This is the way the school savings bank system was started in Richmond, Virginia. Through it, many people learned to save. Some became secure. A few became rich.

Maggie Lena Walker is dead now, but her school savings bank idea lives all over the country.

MAKE A BANK

TO MAKE A BANK YOU WILL NEED THIN CARDBOARD. THE BOTTOM OF A GIFT BOX WHICH MEASURES AT LEAST 13" x 11" IS GOOD TO USE.

① DRAW A GRID OF LINES AS SHOWN

② THEN DRAW THE BANK ON THE GRID IN A DARKER LINE

③ CUT OUT ON DARK LINE

④ CUT SLOT FOR PENNIES IN TOP

⑤ DRAW WINDOWS AND DOORS ON FOUR SQUARES WHICH WILL BE THE SIDES

⑥ FOLD YOUR BANK WHERE YOU SEE DOTTED LINES ON THE GRID

⑦ PASTE THE BOTTOM AND SIDE TABS TO THE INSIDE OF THE BANK

⑧ TUCK IN THE TOP TAB AND YOU ARE READY TO START SAVING YOUR PENNIES

309

Adventures of Isabel

Isabel met an enormous bear,
Isabel, Isabel, didn't care.
The bear was hungry, the bear was ravenous,
The bear's big mouth was cruel and cavernous.
The bear said, Isabel, glad to meet you,
How do, Isabel, now I'll eat you!
Isabel, Isabel, didn't worry;
Isabel didn't scream or scurry.
She washed her hands and she straightened her hair up,
Then Isabel quietly ate the bear up.

—Ogden Nash

310

The Runaway Cow

ELEANOR FRANCES LATTIMORE

Annette, the cow, led a peaceful life. There were no fights for her, and no noisy animals shared her shed. The worst thing that troubled her was being bitten by flies, and of course that was what her long tail was for— shooing them away.

Annette was Julie Brown's special care. Ever since Julie's father had gone to work in New Orleans it had been she who opened the shed door in the morning and drove the cow out to the pasture to graze. And it was Julie who on wet days carried moss to the shed for Annette to chew. Annette especially liked the moss that hung down from the live oak trees. It did not look good to eat, but it seemed to taste good to her.

Annette must have known how much Julie thought of her. Her large, brown eyes looked at Julie very gently, and she never stamped her hoofs or swished her tail around if Julie were nearby.

"Julie has a charm over that cow," said her mother.

"Yes, Julie can do almost anything she likes with that cow," agreed Granny. "She can even ride on her back. I never knew a cow before who would let anyone ride on her back."

It was really true that Julie could ride Annette, just as though the cow were a horse or a mule. When Annette was lying down in the meadow, chewing, Julie could sit on her back and say, "Get up, Annette, and take me for a ride."

And Annette would turn her head to make sure that it was Julie who was sitting on her back. When she had made sure of that, she would slowly stand up. Julie held on with her hands and knees and never fell off. They would go clear across the meadow to where there was a barbed-wire fence separating this piece of land from the next. Annette would look over the fence for a moment, wondering perhaps if the next meadow were greener than this one. Then she would slowly walk back to her resting place. Julie, light as a hummingbird, never troubled her a bit.

Julie's brother, Louis, wished that Annette would take *him* for a ride some time. But Annette would not let Louis ride on her back. She would not let anyone get on her back except Julie.

One morning in school, Louis was having a hard time keeping his mind on his work. It was a beautiful day, just the right kind of day for playing outdoors. Louis wished that he could go for a ride on Annette's back, like Julie, or go fishing in the bayou with his friend Pete. Pete had not come to school this morning. He must have gone fishing or swimming.

Suddenly a shout came from the yard outside, where the older pupils were having their recess. "A runaway horse! A runaway horse!"

Mr. Lovelace, the teacher, frowned and tapped with his ruler on his desk. There was some sort of foolish game going on, he thought. But Louis's head turned toward the open window. His pencil did not want to make words any more. His hand did not want to hold the pencil.

"That's not a horse. It's a cow running away!" shouted another voice. "There's somebody on its back too!"

There was a rustle of excitement through the classroom. The children could not pretend to pay attention to their work. A runaway horse was something to see—but a runaway cow! They all jiggled up and down in their chairs.

Mr. Lovelace went over to the window and looked out. No, it was not a game. "You may all rise from your seats," he said, turning to the children. "Class is dismissed until the cow is caught."

The children did not need to be spoken to twice. Pushing back their chairs, they all scrambled for the door.

The meadow where Annette grazed was in plain sight
of the schoolyard. Annette was usually in plain sight,
too, barely stirring as she bent her head to munch the soft
grass.

Louis looked, and clapped his hands together in
excitement. There was Annette! But she was certainly
stirring now. She was charging towards the barbed-wire
fence as though she meant to knock it down. Her head
was lowered, and her hoofs were flying.

And on Annette's back there was a rider, but it was
not Julie. It was a boy, and he was managing to hold on
in spite of the speed of the angry cow.

314

The children in the schoolyard were jumping up and down. People were hurrying out of the houses along the street. "Pete!" cried Louis. For surely the boy on Annette's back must be Pete.

"That's Pete, all right," said Alfred, beside him. "And he's going to get a bad fall. Oh!"

For just then Annette reached the fence and pulled up with a jerk. Pete went sailing over her head, over the barbed wire, and landed on his back in the meadow beyond.

Two men, cutting across the field from the road, had nearly caught up with the runaway cow. "Catch the cow! Catch her!" everyone was crying. But there was no need to catch Annette now. As soon as she had got rid of her rider, she turned around and pointed her head toward home. Quietly she walked along, as though nothing at all had happened.

Pete was standing up when the two men reached him. He was feeling himself all over to see if he was hurt, and he looked quite surprised to find he wasn't.

"But what were you doing anyway, trying to ride a cow?" said the men. "Don't you know that a cow is not a mule?"

"It all comes of not going to school," said Granny to Louis, when he came home for dinner. "Pete was just fooling around with nothing to do. And he'd seen Julie ride that cow, so he thought he could too."

"How did he ever get on her back?" asked Louis. "Annette never lets *me* get on her back. She starts to roll over."

"Annette forgot to look around," explained Julie. "She thought it was me."

Granny chuckled. "That's a smart cow, though," she said. "As soon as she got up and started to go, she knew she'd made a mistake. Pete is heavier than Julie."

"So she just ran and ran," said Julie. "I saw her."

"Yes," nodded Louis. "I saw her too. She just ran and ran and ran!"

Pete must have known that he, as well as Annette, had made a mistake. He never tried to ride a cow again. When he came to school, he bent over his books like a real scholar. If Louis or Alfred or anyone else started to ask him about the runaway cow, he just went on with his work, and he would not answer.

317

Father of the Symphony

SIBYL CARNABY

There is some question about when Joseph Haydn was born. He usually gave the date as March 31, 1732, but toward the end of his long and eventful life he told a friend that he had really been born on April 1. He had given the earlier day because he did not want people to think of him as an April Fool. Haydn was always able to laugh at himself and this sense of humor is found in much of his music.

We do know for certain that he was born in the village of Rohrau in southern Austria, near the borders of Hungary and what is now Czechoslovakia. His father was a wagon maker and his mother had been a cook in a nearby castle. The Haydns were a musical family. In the evenings young Joseph, his older sister Franziska, and their parents would gather around the fireplace and sing old Austrian folk songs. Mathias Haydn would accompany them on a small harp he had taught himself to play.

Joseph Haydn left this happy home when he was only six. His uncle Johann was a teacher in the town of Hainburg, a two-hour coach trip away. Joseph was to attend school there and board with his aunt and uncle. He would receive musical training from his uncle, who was choirmaster in a church.

The boy was very homesick. His new home was nothing like the one he had left. His uncle was poorly paid and his aunt was unable to hire anyone to help with their many children. The new boarder was expected to run errands and look after the babies. There was never enough food. And Uncle Johann turned out to be an impatient and unpleasant music teacher.

His playmates in Hainburg were no comfort to the lonely boy. They teased him without mercy. How he missed his home in Rohrau! For all the unhappiness of his two years in Hainburg, he was compensated in three important ways. He learned to read and write. He received his first musical training. And he learned how to be self-reliant, to summon up an inner strength with which to face any problem. This inner strength was to help him greatly during the difficult years ahead.

In the year 1740 the choirmaster of St. Stephen's Cathedral in Vienna came to Hainburg. He was scouting for new singers for his famous boys' choir. The eight-year-old Haydn sang for him, reading the music at sight. The choirmaster was impressed not only with the boy's voice but with his ability to sight-read as well.

"Would you like to come to Vienna, my boy?" he asked.

Vienna would mean escape from the hateful town of Hainburg. And it was supposed to be a splendid city. Haydn lost no time in accepting the wonderful offer. He was never to regret it. He fell in love with Vienna and remained in love with it all his life.

The first years there were not easy ones. The seemingly kindly choirmaster turned out to be a very harsh man. The choirboys had to work hard and were given little food. They had to sing at least twice a day in the cathedral. Often they

were taken to homes of the wealthy to give concerts. It was only then that they got enough to eat, for there were always ample refreshments.

The choirboys sang at the palace of the young Empress Maria Theresa several times. Joseph got into trouble by climbing on some boards outside the empress's window. Maria Theresa told the choirmaster that the boy should receive a beating, and the harsh choirmaster was happy to oblige.

Haydn stayed with the choir until 1749. During a rehearsal in that year he cut off the pigtail of the boy in front of him. The choirmaster expelled him immediately. At the age of seventeen, with no money and only the clothes he was wearing, Joseph Haydn was turned out onto the streets of Vienna.

He wandered the streets as the chilly November afternoon turned into a bitterly cold night. He wondered what to do. There was always the warm and happy home in Rohrau. His parents and his sister Franziska would welcome him, but going back home would mean giving up his music. He was now determined to become a composer. That night he slept on a park bench.

321

The very next day his fortunes took a turn for the better.
Michael Spangler, a poor, young music teacher whom
Haydn knew, invited him to share his small apartment. He
stayed there for several months. He earned some money
by playing the violin in the streets of Vienna. Then he had a
stroke of good luck. A friend of his father, learning of his
poverty, loaned him some money. Haydn was able to move
into a room of his own. It was on the sixth floor of an old
building. Walking up six flights of stairs did not dampen the
spirits of the young musician. He was able to buy some
music books and to begin studying in earnest.

Haydn was now playing his violin in small orchestras at
dances and weddings. He was even giving music lessons.
Soon he met Niccolo Porpora, one of the leading
composers and teachers in Vienna. Porpora was seventy

years old and was noted for his bad temper. He offered to give Haydn lessons in writing music. In return, Haydn would assist him at his other lessons—and brush his clothes, polish his boots, and clean his rooms.

The arrangement worked well, and the young man learned much from the gruff old teacher. He learned so well that a wealthy baron asked him to prepare some musical programs for him. He worked for the baron for four years. In 1755 he wrote the first of his many string quartets.

Haydn's bleak years of hunger and cold were now over. All Vienna was talking about the young composer. He continued to give music lessons. He conducted orchestras and wrote music for a popular new instrument, the piano. Often he worked fifteen hours a day. In 1759 his life took a new turn when he became musical director for Count Morzin.

The count had a house in Vienna and a castle in the country. He had an orchestra of sixteen musicians, which Haydn was to conduct and for which he would write music. It seemed a wonderful opportunity for a twenty-seven-year-old composer. In his first year with the count, Haydn wrote the first of his many symphonies.

After two years the count found that keeping an orchestra was too expensive for him. Haydn lost his job but soon found a similar one with Prince Esterhazy. He was to stay with the Esterhazy family for nearly thirty years. He was so popular with the members of the orchestra that they called him Papa Haydn. He wrote most of his symphonies and string quartets during these years.

Haydn has been called the Father of the Symphony. He did not invent the form, but he brought it to new heights. He was to write more than a hundred symphonies. At the

Esterhazy palace he had a fine orchestra to perform them. Often he would give titles to his symphonies—one he called *Morning,* one *Afternoon,* and one *Night.*

One of his symphonies was based on music he had written for the play *The Absent-Minded Man.* There are startling examples of musical absent-mindedness in it. The musicians suddenly break off what they are playing and begin playing something else. The violinists realize that they forgot to tune their instruments, and the music has to be stopped to allow them to tune them. No wonder one of Haydn's friends said, "He could easily discover the comic side of anything."

Haydn wrote operas too. He liked mysterious titles like *The Desert Island* and *The World on the Moon.*

The Esterhazy palace was in Hungary, far from Vienna but not too far from Haydn's birthplace of Rohrau. His father came to visit him and was delighted at his son's success. Another visitor was the Empress Maria Theresa. Haydn wrote a symphony for her. He could not resist reminding her of the time she asked that he be beaten for climbing outside her window when he was a choirboy.

Most of the musicians in the Esterhazy orchestra were from Vienna. At one period they were kept so busy with Haydn's music that many months passed without time off for a visit to their beloved city. Prince Esterhazy promised Haydn that they would have a week off but kept forgetting his promise. So Haydn wrote what came to be known as the *Farewell* Symphony. Toward its end, one by one, the musicians would blow out the candles by their music stands and quietly walk out. Finally the stage was dark—and empty. The prince got the idea and permitted everyone to have a vacation in Vienna.

In Vienna, Haydn met the brilliant young composer Mozart. Although Haydn was twenty-four years older, the two became close friends. Mozart wrote six string quartets for his friend. Haydn told Mozart's father, "Your son is the greatest composer of us all."

In 1790 Haydn's service with the Esterhazy family came to an end. He was invited to visit London and conduct his music there. He was fifty-eight and had never traveled much. He discussed the trip with Mozart, who said "but you don't know the language." To which Haydn replied, "My language is understood everywhere."

Mozart helped him pack and on December 15 saw his friend off on what was to be the greatest adventure of his life.

London was different from Vienna, Haydn soon discovered. In Vienna, music was performed largely in

325

private homes. In London, it was performed in theaters, and thousands came to hear it. Haydn was to conduct dozens of concerts, mostly of his own music. London turned out to see and hear the great Joseph Haydn. He stayed for a year and a half, as success followed success.

During this and his second English visit, in 1794–95, Haydn wrote his last twelve symphonies and conducted their first performances in London. These are the works by which he is best remembered today. They are often referred to as the *London* symphonies.

In one of them the composer's old love of a joke appeared again. During a slow and gentle part the orchestra suddenly plays a loud chord. "To keep the audience awake," explained Haydn. It soon came to be known as the *Surprise* Symphony.

During Haydn's first London visit, Mozart had died suddenly in Vienna. Haydn was heartbroken and was never to completely recover from this loss.

Returning from London the second time, in 1795, Haydn settled in Vienna and wrote several works for chorus and orchestra. More and more honors came to him as the years passed. The poor choirboy who once wandered the streets of Vienna, cold and alone, was now the most famous composer in the world. But a lifetime of hard work had exhausted him. In his last years he rarely went out of his house on a quiet street of Vienna (now called Joseph Haydn Street). On May 31, 1809, he died peacefully in his sleep.

Tributes poured in from everywhere. Perhaps the one the old man would have most liked was a memorial service at a Viennese church at which Mozart's last work, the beautiful *Requiem*, was performed to honor Haydn.

Petronella

JAY WILLIAMS

In the kingdom of Skyclear Mountain, three princes were always born to the king and queen. The oldest prince was always called Michael, the middle prince was always called George, and the youngest was always called Peter. When they were grown, they always went out to seek their fortunes. What happened to the oldest prince and the middle prince no one ever knew. But the youngest prince always rescued a princess, brought her home, and in time ruled over the kingdom. That was the way it had always been. Until now.

Now was the time of King Peter the twenty-sixth and Queen Blossom. An oldest prince was born, and a middle prince. But the youngest prince turned out to be a girl.

329

"Well," said the king gloomily, "we can't call her Peter. We'll have to call her Petronella. And what's to be done about it, I'm sure I don't know."

There was nothing to be done. The years passed, and the time came for the princes to go out and seek their fortunes. Michael and George said good-bye to the king and queen and mounted their horses. Then out came Petronella. She was dressed in traveling clothes, with her bag packed and a sword by her side.

"If you think," she said, "that I'm going to sit at home, you are mistaken. I'm going to seek my fortune, too."

"Impossible!" said the king.

"What will people say?" cried the queen.

"Look," said Prince Michael, "be reasonable, Pet. Stay home. Sooner or later a prince will turn up here."

Petronella smiled. She was a tall, handsome girl with flaming red hair, and when she smiled in that particular way it meant she was trying to keep her temper. "I'm going with you," she said. "I'll find a prince if I have to rescue one from something myself. And that's that."

The grooms brought out her horse, she said good-bye to her parents, and away she went behind her two brothers.

They traveled into the flatlands below Skyclear Mountain. After many days, they entered a great dark forest. They came to a place where the road divided into three, and there at the fork sat a little, wrinkled old man covered with dust and spiderwebs.

Prince Michael said haughtily, "Where do these roads go, old man?"

"The road on the right goes to the city of Gratz," the man replied. "The road in the center goes to the castle of Blitz.

The road on the left goes to the house of Albion the enchanter. And that's one."

"What do you mean by 'And that's one'?" asked Prince George.

"I mean," said the old man, "that I am forced to sit on this spot without stirring, and that I must answer one question from each person who passes by. And that's two."

Petronella's kind heart was touched. "Is there anything I can do to help you?" she asked.

The old man sprang to his feet. The dust fell from him in clouds. "You have already done so," he said. "For that question is the one which releases me. I have sat here for sixty-two years waiting for someone to ask me that." He snapped his fingers with joy. "In return, I will tell you anything you wish to know."

331

"Where can I find a prince?" Petronella said promptly.

"There is one in the house of Albion the enchanter," the old man answered.

"Ah," said Petronella, "then that is where I am going."

"In that case I will leave you," said her oldest brother. "For I am going to the castle of Blitz to see if I can find my fortune there."

"Good luck," said Prince George. "For I am going to the city of Gratz. I have a feeling my fortune is there."

They embraced her and rode away.

Petronella looked thoughtfully at the old man, who was combing spiderwebs and dust out of his beard. "May I ask you something else?" she said.

"Of course. Anything."

"Suppose I wanted to rescue that prince from the enchanter. How would I go about it? I haven't any experience in such things, you see."

The old man chewed a piece of his beard. "I do not know everything," he said, after a moment. "I know that there are three magical secrets which, if you can get them from him, will help you."

"How can I get them?" asked Petronella.

"Offer to work for him. He will set you three tasks, and if you can do them you may demand a reward for each. You must ask him for a comb for your hair, a mirror to look into, and a ring for your finger."

"And then?"

"I do not know. I only know that when you rescue the prince, you can use these things to escape from the enchanter."

"It doesn't sound easy," sighed Petronella.

"Nothing we really want is easy," said the old man.

"Look at me—I have wanted my freedom, and I've had to wait sixty-two years for it."

Petronella said good-bye to him. She mounted her horse and galloped along the third road. It ended at a low, rambling house with a red roof. It was a comfortable-looking house, surrounded by gardens and stables and trees heavy with fruit.

On the lawn, in an armchair, sat a handsome young man with his eyes closed and his face turned to the sky.

Petronella tied her horse to the gate and walked across the lawn. "Is this the house of Albion the enchanter?" she said.

The young man blinked up at her in surprise. "I think so," he said. "Yes, I'm sure it is."

"And who are you?"

The young man yawned and stretched. "I am Prince Ferdinand of Firebright," he replied. "Would you mind stepping aside? I'm trying to get a suntan and you're standing in the way."

Petronella snorted. "You don't sound like much of a prince," she said.

"That's funny," said the young man, closing his eyes. "That's what my father always says."

At that moment the door of the house opened. Out came a man dressed all in black and silver. He was tall and thin, and as sinister as a cloud full of thunder. His face was stern, but full of wisdom. Petronella knew at once that he must be the enchanter.

He bowed to her politely. "What can I do for you?"

"I wish to work for you," said Petronella boldly.

Albion nodded. "I cannot refuse you," he said. "But I warn you, it will be dangerous. Tonight I will give you a task. If you do it, I will reward you. If you fail, you must die."

Petronella glanced at the prince and sighed. "If I must, I must," she said. "Very well."

That evening they all had dinner together in the enchanter's cozy kitchen. Then Albion took Petronella out to a stone building and unbolted its door. Inside were seven huge black dogs. "You must watch my hounds all night," said he.

Petronella went in, and Albion closed and locked the door. At once the hounds began to snarl and bark. They showed their teeth at her. But Petronella was a real princess. Instead of backing away, she went toward the dogs. She began to speak to them in a quiet voice. They stopped snarling and sniffed at her. She patted their heads.

334

"I see what it is," she said. "You are lonely here. I will keep you company." And so all night long, she sat on the floor and talked to the hounds and stroked them. They lay close to her, panting.

In the morning Albion came and let her out. "Ah," said he, "I see that you are brave. If you had run from the dogs, they would have torn you to pieces. Now you may ask for what you want."

"I want a comb for my hair," said Petronella.

The enchanter gave her a comb carved from a piece of black wood.

Prince Ferdinand was sunning himself and working at a crossword puzzle. Petronella said to him in a low voice, "I am doing this for you."

"That's nice," said the prince. "What's 'selfish' in nine letters?"

"You are," snapped Petronella. She went to the enchanter. "I will work for you once more," she said.

That night Albion led her to a stable. Inside were seven huge horses. "Tonight," he said, "you must watch my steeds."

He went out and locked the door. At once the horses began to rear and neigh. They pawed at her with their iron hoofs. But Petronella was a real princess. She looked closely at them and saw that their coats were rough and their manes and tails full of burrs. "I see what it is," she said. "You are hungry and dirty."

She brought them as much hay as they could eat, and began to brush them. All night long she fed them and groomed them, and they stood quietly in their stalls.

In the morning Albion let her out. "You are as kind as you are brave," said he. "If you had run from them, they would have trampled you under their hoofs. What will you have as a reward?"

"I want a mirror to look into," said Petronella.

The enchanter gave her a mirror made of gray silver.

She looked across the lawn at Prince Ferdinand. He was doing sitting-up exercises. He was certainly handsome. She said to the enchanter, "I will work for you once more."

That night Albion led her to a loft above the stables. There, on perches, were seven great hawks. "Tonight," said he, "you must watch my falcons."

As soon as Petronella was locked in, the hawks began to beat their wings and scream at her. Petronella laughed. "That is not how birds sing," she said. "Listen." She began to sing in a sweet voice. The hawks fell silent. All night long she sang to them, and they sat like feathered statues on their perches, listening.

In the morning Albion said, "You are as talented as you are kind and brave. If you had run from them, they would have pecked and clawed you without mercy. What do you want now?"

"I want a ring for my finger," said Petronella.

The enchanter gave her a ring made from a single diamond.

All that day and all that night Petronella slept, for she was very tired. But early the next morning, she crept into Prince Ferdinand's room. "Wake up," whispered Petronella. "I am going to rescue you."

337

Ferdinand awoke and stared sleepily at her. "What time is it?"

"Never mind that," said Petronella. "Come on!"

"But I'm sleepy," Ferdinand objected. "And it's so pleasant here."

Petronella shook her head. "You're not much of a prince," she said grimly. "But you're the best I can do."

She grabbed him by the wrist and dragged him out of bed. She hauled him down the stairs and saddled their horses quickly. She gave the prince a shove, and he mounted. She

jumped on her own horse, seized the prince's reins, and
away they went like the wind.

They had not gone far when they heard a tremendous
thumping. Petronella looked back. A dark cloud rose behind
them, and beneath it she saw the enchanter. He was running
with great strides, faster than the horses could go.

Petronella desperately pulled out the comb. And because
she didn't know what else to do with it, she threw it on the
ground. At once a forest rose up. The trees were so thick that
no one could get between them.

Away went Petronella and the prince. But the enchanter turned himself into an ax and began to chop. Right and left he chopped, flashing, and the trees fell before him. Soon he was through the wood, and once again Petronella heard his footsteps thumping behind.

She reined in the horses. She took out the mirror and threw it on the ground. At once a wide lake spread out behind them, gray and glittering.

Off they went again. But the enchanter sprang into the water, turning himself into a salmon as he did so. He swam across the lake and leaped out of the water on to the other bank. Petronella heard him coming—*thump! thump!*—behind them again.

This time she threw down the ring. It didn't turn into anything, but lay shining on the ground. The enchanter came running up. And as he jumped over the ring, it opened wide and then snapped up around him. It held his arms tight to his body, in a magical grip from which he could not escape.

"Well," said Prince Ferdinand, "that's the end of him."

Petronella looked at him in annoyance. Then she looked at the enchanter, held fast in the ring. "Bother!" she said. "I can't just leave him here. He'll starve to death."

She got off her horse and went up to him. "If I release you," she said, "will you promise to let the prince go free?"

Albion stared at her in astonishment. "Let him go free?" he said. "What are you talking about? I'm glad to get rid of him."

It was Petronella's turn to look surprised. "I don't understand," she said. "Weren't you holding him prisoner?"

"Certainly not," said Albion. "He came to visit me for a weekend. At the end of it, he said, 'It's so pleasant here, do you mind if I stay on for another day or two?' I'm very polite and I said, 'Of course.' He stayed on, and on, and on. I didn't like to be rude to a guest and I couldn't just kick him out. I don't know what I'd have done if you hadn't dragged him away.''

"But then—" said Petronella, "but then—why did you come running after him this way?"

"I wasn't chasing him," said the enchanter. "I was chasing *you*. You are just the girl I've been looking for. You are brave and kind and talented, and beautiful as well."

"Oh," said Petronella. "I see. How do I get this ring off you?"

"Give me a kiss."

She did so. The ring vanished from around Albion and reappeared on Petronella's finger. "I don't know what my parents will say when I come home with you instead of a prince," she said.

"Let's go and find out, shall we?" said the enchanter cheerfully.

He mounted one horse and Petronella the other. And off they trotted, side by side, leaving Prince Ferdinand of Firebright to walk home as best he could.

342

Unit Eight
Disasters

The Glittering Cloud

LAURA INGALLS WILDER

At the time this story takes place, Laura Ingalls lives on a farm in
Minnesota with her Ma and Pa and her sisters, Mary and baby Carrie.
The family had lived in a dugout on Plum Creek until Pa built them
a board house with glass windows. Now their money is running low
and their hopes are pinned on the fast-ripening wheat crop.

Now the wheat was almost ready to cut.

Every day Pa looked at it. Every night he talked about it, and showed Laura some long, stiff wheat-heads. The plump grains were getting harder in their little husks. Pa said the weather was perfect for ripening wheat.

"If this keeps up," he said, "we'll start harvesting next week."

The weather was very hot. The thin, high sky was too hot to look at. Air rose up in waves from the whole prairie, as it does from a hot stove. In the schoolhouse the children panted like lizards, and the sticky pine-juice dripped down the board walls.

Saturday morning Laura went walking with Pa to look at the wheat. It was almost as tall as Pa. He lifted her onto his shoulder so that she could see over the heavy, bending tops. The field was greeny gold.

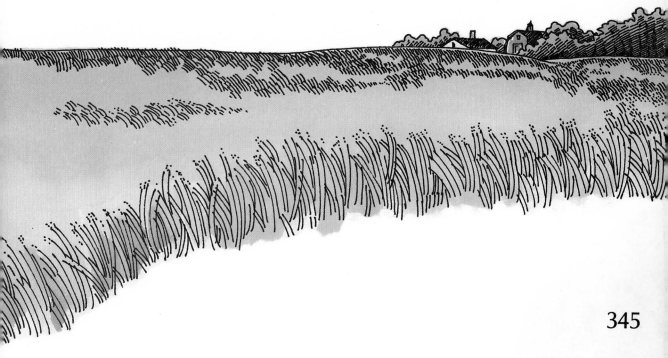

At the dinner table Pa told Ma about it. He had never seen such a crop. There were forty bushels to the acre, and wheat was a dollar a bushel. They were rich now. This was a wonderful country. Now they could have anything they wanted. Laura listened and thought, now Pa would get his new boots.

She sat facing the open door and the sunshine streaming through it. Something seemed to dim the sunshine. Laura rubbed her eyes and looked again. The sunshine really was dim. It grew dimmer until there was no sunshine.

"I do believe a storm is coming up," said Ma. "There must be a cloud over the sun."

Pa got up quickly and went to the door. A storm might hurt the wheat. He looked out, then he went out.

The light was queer. It was not like the changed light before a storm. The air did not press down as it did before a storm. Laura was frightened, she did not know why.

She ran outdoors, where Pa stood looking up at the sky. Ma and Mary came out, too, and Pa asked, "What do you make of that, Caroline?"

A cloud was over the sun. It was not like any cloud they had ever seen before. It was a cloud of something like snowflakes, but they were larger than snowflakes, and thin and glittering. Light shone through each flickering particle.

There was no wind. The grasses were still and the hot air did not stir, but the edge of the cloud came on across the sky faster than wind. The hair stood up on Jack's neck. All at once he made a frightful sound up at that cloud, a growl and a whine.

Plunk! something hit Laura's head and fell to the
ground. She looked down and saw the largest
grasshopper she had ever seen. Then huge brown
grasshoppers were hitting the ground all around her,
hitting her head and her face and her arms. They came
thudding down like hail.

The cloud was hailing grasshoppers. The cloud *was*
grasshoppers. Their bodies hid the sun and made
darkness. Their thin, large wings gleamed and glittered.
The rasping whirring of their wings filled the whole air
and they hit the ground and the house with the noise of a
hailstorm.

Laura tried to beat them off. Their claws clung to her
skin and her dress. They looked at her with bulging eyes,
turning their heads this way and that. Mary ran
screaming into the house. Grasshoppers covered the
ground, there was not one bare bit to step on. Laura had
to step on grasshoppers and they smashed squirming and
slimy under her feet.

Ma was slamming the windows shut, all around the house. Pa came and stood just inside the front door, looking out. Laura and Jack stood close beside him. Grasshoppers beat down from the sky and swarmed thick over the ground. Their long wings were folded and their strong legs took them hopping everywhere. The air whirred and the roof went on sounding like a roof in a hailstorm.

Then Laura heard another sound, one big sound made of tiny nips and snips and gnawings.

"The wheat!" Pa shouted. He dashed out the back door and ran toward the wheat-field.

The grasshoppers were eating. You could not hear one grasshopper eat, unless you listened very carefully while you held him and fed him grass. Millions and millions of grasshoppers were eating now. You could hear the millions of jaws biting and chewing.

Pa came running back to the stable. Through the window Laura saw him hitching Sam and David to the wagon. He began pitching old dirty hay from the manure-pile into the wagon, as fast as he could. Ma ran out, took the other pitchfork and helped him. Then he drove away to the wheat-field and Ma followed the wagon.

Pa drove around the field, throwing out little piles of stuff as he went. Ma stooped over one, then a thread of smoke rose from it and spread. Ma lighted pile after pile. Laura watched till a smudge of smoke hid the field and Ma and Pa and the wagon.

Grasshoppers were still falling from the sky. The light was still dim because grasshoppers covered the sun.

Ma came back to the house, and in the closed lean-to

348

she took off her dress and her petticoats and killed the
grasshoppers she shook out of them. She had lighted fires
all around the wheat-field. Perhaps smoke would keep
the grasshoppers from eating the wheat.

Ma and Mary and Laura were quiet in the shut,
smothery house. Carrie was so little that she cried, even
in Ma's arms. She cried herself to sleep. Through the
walls came the sound of grasshoppers eating.

The darkness went away. The sun shone again. All
over the ground was a crawling, hopping mass of
grasshoppers. They were eating all the soft, short grass
off the knoll. The tall prairie grasses swayed and bent
and fell.

"Oh, look," Laura said, low, at the window.

They were eating the willow tops. The willows' leaves
were thin and bare twigs stuck out. Then whole branches
were bare and knobby with masses of grasshoppers.

349

"I don't want to look any more," Mary said, and she went away from the window. Laura did not want to look any more, either, but she could not stop looking.

The hens were funny. The two hens and their gawky pullets were eating grasshoppers with all their might. They were used to stretching their necks out low and running fast after grasshoppers and not catching them. Every time they stretched out now, they got a grasshopper right then. They were surprised. They kept stretching out their necks and trying to run in all directions at once.

"Well, we won't have to buy feed for the hens," said Ma. "There's no great loss without some gain."

The green garden rows were wilting down. The potatoes, the carrots, the beets and beans were being eaten away. The long leaves were eaten off the cornstalks, and the tassels, and the ears of young corn in their green husks fell covered with grasshoppers.

There was nothing anybody could do about it.

Smoke still hid the wheat-field. Sometimes Laura saw Pa moving dimly in it. He stirred up the smouldering fires and thick smoke hid him again.

When it was time to go for Spot, Laura put on stockings and shoes and a shawl. Spot was standing in the old ford of Plum Creek, shaking her skin and switching her tail. The herd went mournfully lowing beyond the old dugout. Laura was sure that cattle could not eat grass so full of grasshoppers. If the grasshoppers ate all the grass, the cattle would starve.

Grasshoppers were thick under her petticoats and on her dress and shawl. She kept striking them off her face and hands. Her shoes and Spot's feet crunched grasshoppers.

Ma came out in a shawl to do the milking. Laura helped her. They could not keep grasshoppers out of the milk. Ma had brought a cloth to cover the pail but they could not keep it covered while they milked into it. Ma skimmed out the grasshoppers with a tin cup.

Grasshoppers went into the house with them. Their clothes were full of grasshoppers. Some jumped onto the hot stove where Mary was starting supper. Ma covered the food till they had chased and smashed every grasshopper. She swept them up and shoveled them into the stove.

Pa came into the house long enough to eat supper while Sam and David were eating theirs. Ma did not ask him what was happening to the wheat. She only smiled and said: "Don't worry, Charles. We've always got along."

Pa's throat rasped and Ma said: "Have another cup of tea, Charles. It will help get the smoke out of your throat."

When Pa had drunk the tea, he went back to the wheat-field with another load of old hay and manure.

In bed, Laura and Mary could still hear the whirring and snipping and chewing. Laura felt claws crawling on her. There were no grasshoppers in bed, but she could not brush the feeling off her arms and cheeks. In the dark she saw grasshoppers' bulging eyes and felt their claws crawling until she went to sleep.

Pa was not downstairs next morning. All night he had been working to keep the smoke over the wheat, and he did not come to breakfast. He was still working.

The whole prairie was changed. The grasses did not wave, they had fallen in ridges. The rising sun made all the prairie rough with shadows where the tall grasses had sunk against each other.

The willow trees were bare. In the plum thickets only a few plumpits hung to the leafless branches. The nipping, clicking, gnawing sound of the grasshoppers' eating was still going on.

At noon Pa came driving the wagon out of the smoke. He put Sam and David into the stable, and slowly came to the house. His face was black with smoke and his eyeballs were red. He hung his hat on the nail behind the door and sat down at the table.

"It's no use, Caroline," he said. "Smoke won't stop them. They keep dropping down through it and hopping in from all sides. The wheat is falling now. They're cutting it off like a scythe. And eating it, straw and all."

He put his elbows on the table and hid his face with his hands. Laura and Mary sat still. Only Carrie on her high stool rattled her spoon and reached her little hand toward the bread. She was too young to understand.

"Never mind, Charles," Ma said. "We've been through hard times before."

Laura looked down at Pa's patched boots under the table and her throat swelled and ached. Pa could not have new boots now.

Pa's hands came down from his face and he picked up his knife and fork. His beard smiled, but his eyes would not twinkle. They were dull and dim.

"Don't worry, Caroline," he said. "We did all we could, and we'll pull through somehow."

353

Then Laura remembered that the new house was not paid for. Pa had said he would pay for it when he harvested the wheat.

It was a quiet meal, and when it was over Pa lay down on the floor and went to sleep. Ma slipped a pillow under his head and laid her finger on her lips to tell Laura and Mary to be still.

They took Carrie into the bedroom and kept her quiet with their paper dolls. The only sound was the sound of the grasshoppers' eating.

Day after day the grasshoppers kept on eating. They ate all the wheat and the oats. They ate every green thing—all the garden and all the prairie grass.

"Oh, Pa, what will the rabbits do?" Laura asked. "And the poor birds?"

"Look around you, Laura," Pa said.

The rabbits had all gone away. The little birds of the grass tops were gone. The birds that were left were eating grasshoppers. And prairie hens ran with outstretched necks, gobbling grasshoppers.

When Sunday came, Pa and Laura and Mary walked to Sunday school. The sun shone so bright and hot that Ma said she would stay at home with Carrie, and Pa left Sam and David in the shady stable.

There had been no rain for so long that Laura walked across Plum Creek on dry stones. The whole prairie was bare and brown. Millions of brown grasshoppers whirred low over it. Not a green thing was in sight anywhere.

All the way, Laura and Mary brushed off grasshoppers. When they came to the church, brown grasshoppers were thick on their petticoats. They lifted their skirts and brushed them off before they went in. But careful as they were, the grasshoppers had spit tobacco-juice on their best Sunday dresses.

Nothing would take out the horrid stains. They would have to wear their best dresses with the brown spots on them.

Many people in town were going back East. Christy and Cassie had to go. Laura said good-bye to Christy and Mary said good-bye to Cassie, their best friends.

They did not go to school any more. They must save their shoes for winter and they could not bear to walk barefooted on grasshoppers. School would be ended soon, anyway, and Ma said she would teach them through the winter so they would not be behind their classes when school opened again next spring.

Pa worked for Mr. Nelson and earned the use of Mr. Nelson's plough. He began to plough the bare wheat-field, to make it ready for next year's wheat crop.

The Big Wave

PEARL S. BUCK

Kino, a Japanese boy, lives on a hillside overlooking the sea. His friend Jiya lives in the fishing village at the foot of the hill. Twenty miles away from the village is a volcano. Even though it has been quiet for years, it is a constant threat.

On days when the sky was bright and the winds mild the ocean lay so calm and blue that it was hard to believe that it could be cruel and angry. Yet even Kino never quite forgot that under the warm blue surface the water was cold and green. When the sun shone the deep water was still. But when the deep water moved and heaved and stirred, ah, then Kino was glad that his father was a farmer and not a fisherman.

And yet, one day, it was the earth that brought the big wave. Deep under the deepest part of the ocean, miles under the still green waters, fires raged in the heart of the earth. The icy cold of the water could not chill those fires. Rocks were melted and boiled under the crust of the ocean's bed, under the weight of the water, but they could not break through. At last the steam grew so strong that it forced its way through to the mouth of the volcano. That day, as he helped his father plant turnips, Kino saw the sky overcast halfway to the zenith.

"Look, Father!" he cried. "The volcano is burning again!"

His father stopped and gazed anxiously at the sky. "It looks very angry," he said. "I shall not sleep tonight."

357

All night while the others slept, Kino's father kept watch. When it was dark, the sky was lit with red and the earth trembled under the farmhouses. Down at the fishing village lights in the little houses showed that other fathers watched, too. For generations fathers had watched earth and sea.

Morning came, a strange fiery dawn. The sky was red and gray, and even here upon the farms cinders and ash fell from the volcano. Kino had a strange feeling, when he stepped barefoot upon the earth, that it was hot under his feet. In the house the mother had taken down everything from the walls that could fall or be broken, and her few good dishes she had packed into straw in a basket and set outside.

"Shall we have an earthquake, Father?" Kino asked as they ate breakfast.

"I cannot tell, my son," his father replied. "Earth and sea are struggling together against the fires inside the earth."

358

No fishing boats set sail that hot summer morning. There was no wind. The sea lay dead and calm, as though oil had been poured upon the waters. It was a purple gray, suave and beautiful, but when Kino looked at it he felt afraid.

"Why is the sea such a color?" he asked.

"Sea mirrors sky," his father replied. "Sea and earth and sky—if they work together against man, it will be dangerous indeed for us."

"Where are the gods at such a time?" Kino asked. "Will they not be mindful of us?"

"There are times when the gods leave man to take care of himself," his father replied. "They test us, to see how able we are to save ourselves."

"And if we are not able?" Kino asked.

"We must be able," his father replied. "Fear alone makes man weak. If you are afraid, your hands tremble, your feet falter, and your brain cannot tell hands and feet what to do."

359

No one stirred from home that day. Kino's father sat at the door, watching the sky and the oily sea, and Kino stayed near him. He did not know what Jiya was doing, but he imagined that Jiya, too, stayed by his father. So the hours passed until noon.

At noon his father pointed down the mountainside. "Look at Old Gentleman's castle," he said.

Halfway down the mountainside on the knoll where the castle stood, Kino now saw a red flag rise slowly to the top of a tall pole and hang limp against the gray sky.

"Old Gentleman is telling everyone to be ready," Kino's father went on. "Twice have I seen that flag go up, both times before you were born."

"Be ready for what?" Kino asked in a frightened voice.

"For whatever happens," Kino's father replied.

At two o'clock the sky began to grow black. The air was as hot as though a forest fire were burning, but there was no sign of such a fire. The glow of the volcano glared over the mountaintop, blood-red against the black. A deep-toned bell tolled over the hills.

"What is that bell?" Kino asked his father. "I never heard it before."

"It rang twice before you were born," his father replied. "It is the bell in the temple inside the walls of Old Gentleman's castle. He is calling the people to come up out of the village and shelter within his walls."

"Will they come?" Kino asked.

"Not all of them," his father replied. "Parents will try to make their children go, but the children will not want to leave their parents. Mothers will not want to leave fathers, and the fathers will stay by their boats. But some will want to be sure of life."

The bell kept on ringing urgently, and soon out of the village a trickling stream of people, nearly all of them children, began to climb toward the knoll.

"I wish Jiya would come," Kino said. "Do you think he will see me if I stand on the edge of the terrace and wave my white girdle cloth?"

"Try it," his father said.

"Come with me," Kino begged.

So Kino and his father stood on the edge of the terrace and waved. Kino took off the strip of white cloth from about his waist that he wore instead of a belt, and he waved it, holding it in both hands, high above his head.

Far down the hill Jiya saw the two figures and the waving strip of white against the dark sky. He was crying as he climbed, and trying not to cry. He had not wanted to leave his father, but because he was the youngest one, his older brother and his father and mother had all told him that he must go up the mountain. "We must divide ourselves," Jiya's father said. "If the ocean yields to the fires you must live after us."

"I don't want to live alone," Jiya said.

"It is your duty to obey me, as a good Japanese son," his father told him.

Jiya had run out of the house, crying. Now when he saw Kino, he decided that he would go there instead of to the castle, and he began to hurry up the hill to the farm. Next to his own family he loved Kino's strong father and kind mother. He had no sister of his own and he thought Setsu was the prettiest girl he had ever seen.

Kino's father put out his hand to help Jiya up the stone wall and Kino was just about to shout out his welcome when suddenly a hurricane wind broke out of the ocean.

361

Kino and Jiya clung together and wrapped their arms about the father's waist.

"Look—look—what is that?" Kino screamed.

The purple rim of the ocean seemed to lift and rise against the clouds. A silver-green band of bright sky appeared like a low dawn above the sea.

"May the gods save us," Kino heard his father mutter. The castle bell began to toll again, deep and pleading. Ah, but would the people hear it in the roaring wind? Their houses had no windows toward the sea. Did they know what was about to happen?

Under the deep waters of the ocean, miles down under the cold, the earth had yielded at last to the fire. It groaned and split open and the cold water fell into the middle of the boiling rocks. Steam burst out and lifted the ocean high into the sky in a big wave. It rushed toward the shore, green and solid, frothing into white at its edges. It rose, higher and higher, lifting up hands and claws.

"I must tell my father!" Jiya screamed.

But Kino's father held him fast with both arms. "It is too late," he said sternly.

And he would not let Jiya go.

In a few seconds, before their eyes the wave had grown and come nearer and nearer, higher and higher. The air was filled with its roar and shout. It rushed over the flat still waters of the ocean and before Jiya could scream again it reached the village and covered it fathoms deep in swirling wild water, green laced with fierce white foam. The wave ran up the mountainside, until the knoll where the castle stood was an island. All who were still climbing the path

were swept away—black, tossing scraps in the wicked waters. The wave ran up the mountain until Kino and Jiya saw the wavelets curl at the terrace walls upon which they stood. Then with a great sucking sigh, the wave swept back again, ebbing into the ocean, dragging everything with it, trees and stones and houses. They stood, the man and the two boys, utterly silent, clinging together, facing the wave as it went away. It swept back over the village and returned slowly again to the ocean, subsiding, sinking into a great stillness.

Upon the beach where the village stood not a house remained, no wreckage of wood or fallen stone wall, no little street of shops, no docks, not a single boat. The beach was as clean of houses as if no human beings had ever lived there. All that had been was now no more.

Jiya gave a wild cry and Kino felt him slip to the ground. He was unconscious. What he had seen was too much for him. What he knew, he could not bear. His family and his home were gone.

Kino began to cry and Kino's father did not stop him. He stooped and gathered Jiya into his arms and carried him into the house, and Kino's mother ran out of the kitchen and put down a mattress and Kino's father laid Jiya upon it.

"It is better that he is unconscious," he said gently. "Let him remain so until his own will wakes him. I will sit by him."

"I will rub his hands and feet," Kino's mother said sadly.

Kino could say nothing. He was still crying and his father let him cry for a while. Then he said to his wife:

"Heat a little rice soup for Kino and put some ginger in it. He feels cold."

Now Kino did not know until his father spoke that he did

feel cold. He was shivering and he could not stop crying. Setsu came in. She had not seen the big wave, for her mother had closed the windows and drawn the curtains against the sea. But now she saw Jiya lying white-pale and still.

"Is Jiya dead?" she asked.

"No, Jiya is living," her father replied.

"Why doesn't he open his eyes?" she asked again.

"Soon he will open his eyes," the father replied.

"If Jiya is not dead, why does Kino cry?" Setsu asked.

"You are asking too many questions," her father told her. "Go back to the kitchen and help your mother."

So Setsu went back again, sucking her forefinger, and staring at Jiya and Kino as she went and soon the mother came in with the hot rice soup and Kino drank it. He felt warm now and he could stop crying. But he was still frightened and sad.

"What will we say to Jiya when he wakes?" he asked his father.

"We will not talk," his father replied. "We will give him warm food and let him rest. We will help him to feel he still has a home."

"Here?" Kino asked.

"Yes," his father replied. "I have always wanted another son, and Jiya will be that son. As soon as he knows that this is his home, then we must help him to understand what has happened."

Krakatoa

F. H. POUGH

Volcanoes don't all erupt in exactly the same way, and the loss of life they cause isn't always due to one huge explosion. When Krakatoa blew up in 1883, tens of thousands of people lost their lives, not by burning or suffocation but by drowning.

Krakatoa was a wooded island lying in a narrow strip of sea between Java and Sumatra. It had been built up to a height of 2600 feet by the slow growth of several volcanoes that joined together. But it was not a large island and was not settled, though people often went there to pick wild fruit. Everybody knew Krakatoa to be a volcano. There were even some vents from which people sometimes saw steam and dust escaping. But since there had been no eruption for 200 years, everybody considered the volcano finished.

Inside, however, all was not peace and quiet. While the unsuspecting world went about its business, the biggest explosion of modern times was slowly building up. Scientists are not sure exactly what happened. But everything leads them to believe that the eruption of Krakatoa was a steam explosion. The volcano exploded just like a boiler that bursts when the pressure of steam inside it becomes too great.

It is easy enough to see how it could happen. The surface rocks of Krakatoa had long been full of sea water. It had seeped in wherever there was a crack or crevice. That in itself was harmless. But combined with heat it meant trouble. Heat would cause the water in the rocks to turn to steam. The steam would get superheated and expand. It would press more and more on the enclosing rock. Finally the rock would be unable to stand the strain anymore. The rock would give way and there would be a mighty explosion.

In May 1883 a rise of lava provided the heat necessary to start things going. Slowly the steam began to form. To the outside world it looked only as if Krakatoa had suddenly come alive and was erupting like any other volcano. And, indeed, that's exactly what it was doing at first. It erupted with loud noises that could be heard a hundred miles away. Smoke poured out to a height of seven miles. Dust fell 300 miles away. For fourteen weeks Krakatoa kept that up, booming and fuming—sometimes more, sometimes less. But all this was just the overture.

On Sunday, August 26, the island retired behind a cloud of black vapor. There were exploding sounds behind the curtain. Lightning kept ripping through the vapor. Stones dropped from the sky. The big explosions, however, were being reserved for the next day.

There were four of them, all very violent. The third was the most violent of all. There is nothing with which that third boom can be compared. It was said to be the loudest noise ever heard on this planet. Three thousand miles away on the island of Rodriguez, a coast guard heard that sound and carefully noted the time. It was four hours after the explosion. That's how long it took for the sound to travel a distance as far as from San Francisco to New York.

With that third mighty explosion the dust of Krakatoa shot higher up into the sky than anything from the earth had done since humans had been there to see it. It soared seventeen miles up, perhaps more. And there it stayed. It was up so high that it couldn't come down at once. The winds at that level blow with a speed much greater than a hurricane. They seized the dust and swept it on. They swept it all around the earth. In thirteen days the cloud was back where it had started.

But even then the dust didn't fall. The winds carried it on and on, around and around the earth—a dozen times perhaps. It was two full years before the last of Krakatoa sifted back to earth. The thick dust in the upper atmosphere shut out so much sunlight that the world's temperature dropped thirteen degrees that year. All over the earth the sunsets were blood red on account of the dust.

But these were the far-off effects. The explosion had disturbed the waves of the sea as well as those of the air. On the low-lying shores bordering the Sunda Strait, between Java and Sumatra, terrible things were happening. People had hardly got over the shock of the noise when a mountainous wave broke over the shores. There was neither time to flee nor a place to escape to. In a few minutes the sea was sweeping far inland. Villages and towns crumbled. Before the water had returned to the sea, 36,000 people had been drowned.

Behind its pall of dust Krakatoa had not yet stopped erupting, but it was running down. In a few days it would be altogether still. The "bursting of the boiler" had been its last mighty effort. It had almost wiped the island off the earth. Where the volcano had once risen to 2600 feet, there was now just a hole. It was filled with water 900 feet deep!

How Your Body Heals Itself

JOANNA COLE

You will probably get many cuts, scrapes, bruises, and burns in your lifetime. You might even break a bone or two. No matter how many minor injuries you get, they always heal. Your cut closes, your bruise fades away, your bone mends. But it doesn't happen by magic. It is your body itself that works to repair the damage. In some ways your body is like a machine. Your joints move like hinges, your heart works like a pump, even your brain is something like a computer. But there are some important differences. One of these is that when your body is injured, it does not need to be repaired like a machine. It can repair itself because it is alive.

Cells in Your Body

Your body is made of billions of tiny living cells. These cells are so small they can be seen only under a microscope. There are many kinds of cells in the body. They have different shapes and sizes, and they do different jobs. But all cells are made of a jellylike material called *protoplasm,* surrounded by a cell membrane. There are cells in every part of your body.

DIFFERENT KINDS OF CELLS

red blood cells

bone cells

brain cells

surface skin cells

369

Even your blood has cells. Red blood cells carry oxygen to all parts of your body and give the blood its red color. There are other kinds of cells in the blood too. Some of these act like an army on standby, ready to protect you from disease or injury.

How a Cut Heals

You are climbing a fence when a sharp edge cuts your finger. You yell, "Ow!" and pull back your hand. The sharp edge has cut through two levels of skin: the surface layer of your skin, called the *epidermis,* and the inner layer, the *dermis.* The dermis contains nerves—which are sensitive to pain, heat and touch—and microscopic blood vessels called *capillaries.*

Even though you know the cut will heal, you still might feel a little scared when you see blood coming out. But the blood itself contains the substances needed to heal the cut. Like a microscopic rescue team, special cells are already at work.

Stopping the Bleeding

First to the rescue are tiny blood cells called *platelets.* Usually, platelets flow smoothly through the blood-

370

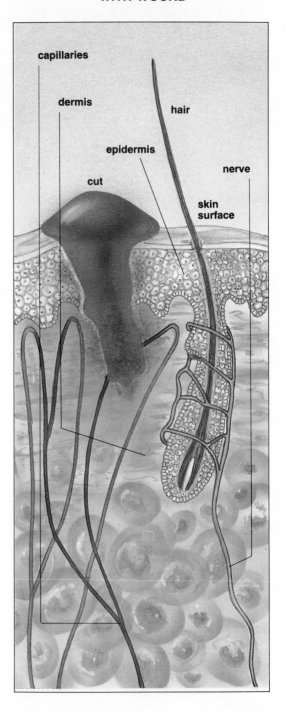

capillaries

dermis

hair

epidermis

nerve

cut

skin surface

stream. But when they touch a rough surface—such as the edges of a broken or cut blood vessel—the platelets change. They become sticky. They stick to the edges of the injured vessels. More and more platelets flow to the vessels. They pile up until they form a clump that acts like a plug. That is why a small cut stops bleeding all by itself in a minute or two. If the body did not have its own way of plugging leaks, you could lose all your blood from even a small cut.

After the bleeding has stopped, your cut is still filled with liquid blood. Now this blood starts to clot, or *coagulate;* that is, it changes from a liquid to a jellylike substance called a *clot.* In the clot, tiny fibers (threadlike strands) form a net that holds the sides of the cut together. This net helps keep the cut from opening and starting to bleed again.

After several hours, the surface of the clot dries out. It becomes a scab. You may not think of a scab as useful, but it is actually an important part of the healing process. The scab acts like a hard shield that protects the injured area.

Underneath the scab, the healing really begins. Other blood cells start entering the cut from nearby blood vessels. These new cells are the white blood cells. They are able to destroy bacteria, or germs, and to carry away bits of dirt.

Fighting the Invaders

Almost every cut has bacteria and dirt in it. The sharp edge of a fence, for example, may have been brushed by an animal, which left bacteria on it. Bits of dust and soil, too small for us to see, are on it too. When you cut yourself on the fence, some of the bacteria and dirt get into the cut.

The white blood cells, which destroy dirt and bacteria, are different from other cells in your body. For one thing, they can "swim." To do this, part of the cell pushes out like an arm in one direction. Then the rest of the cell flows into it. Another "arm" reaches out, and the cell body follows. In this way, a white blood cell can swim through the blood.

When you hurt yourself, white blood cells travel to the blood vessels near the cut. To do its job, a white cell needs to get out of the vessel and swim into the damaged area. It does this by pushing an "arm" between the cells that make up the blood-vessel wall. In a few minutes, the whole white cell squeezes through.

Once they are free, the white cells swim into the cut. There they actually begin eating bacteria and particles of dirt by engulfing them—drawing them inside their cell membranes.

When the bacteria are inside, they are broken down by digestive juices that are very similar to those used to digest food in your stomach.

All this is happening without your even being aware of it. You may be going to school, eating lunch, or reading a book, and all the time an invisible battle is going on inside you!

But still the cut is not fully healed. A cut not only opens up the body to bacteria that must be destroyed. It also causes damage that must be repaired. As the white cells continue their work, other cells begin to repair the gap left in the body's surface.

Repairing the Damage

Up to now, the gap has been covered by the scab. Now surface skin cells at the edges of the cut actually begin sliding under the scab to form a layer of new skin over the cut. To get to the open area, skin cells will even slide over each other. Then other skin cells replace them by multiplying—splitting in half to form new cells.

Meanwhile, the white cells have been finishing up their work of killing the bacteria. Now a new kind of white cell enters the wound. These are the "undertakers," or clean-up crew. They eat up old fibers, bits of damaged cells and dead white cells from the first crew, the bacteria-eating cells, which live only a few days.

By this time the cut is clean, and a very thin layer of surface skin has formed. But the damaged area under it in the inner layer of the skin—the dermis—is still not repaired. Now long thin cells—*fibroblasts* or "fiber-makers"—start arriving from the surrounding skin. These cells manufacture strands of tough, flexible material called *collagen,* which forms a kind of bridge to bind the edges of the gap together.

In about a week the cut is almost completely repaired, and the scab sloughs off. For a while the fiber-makers keep working to strengthen

THREE STAGES OF STOPPING THE BLEEDING

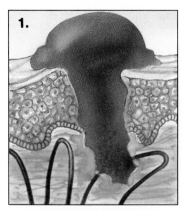

Platelet plug forms

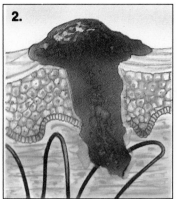

Blood clot forms

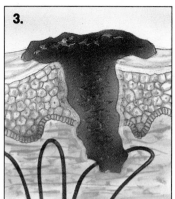

Scab forms

the area with bundles of collagen.

A newly healed cut often looks pink for a time, especially in a light-skinned person. This is because many new blood vessels were formed during the healing process to bring healing blood to the area. The surface skin is thinner than usual right after healing, so the extra amount of blood is quite visible through the new skin.

As time passes, the extra blood vessels gradually disappear. More and more skin cells are added to the surface layer, and eventually the skin becomes as thick as it was before. Then you are no longer able to see the place where the cut was.

When you know how an ordinary small cut heals, you know how almost every injury heals. First the bleeding is stopped. Then various kinds of cells work to clean up dirt and kill bacteria. Finally the damaged area is rebuilt. Serious injuries take longer to heal than minor ones, but the healing process is the same for a tiny paper cut, a skinned knee, or a deep wound.

Everyone gets little cuts and scrapes. They heal quickly, and we usually don't think much about it. But even though we take the healing process for granted, our lives would not be possible without it. Even small injuries would be life threatening: they would stay open to infection, and damage would never be repaired.

We think of doctors as healers, and doctors can help the body heal. In the end, however, it is the body itself that makes its own repairs through the amazing healing process.

373

Some Adventures
of Flat Stanley

JEFF BROWN

Breakfast was ready.

"I will go and wake the boys," Mrs. Lambchop said to her husband, George Lambchop. Just then their younger son, Arthur, called from the bedroom he shared with his brother Stanley. "Hey! Come and look! Hey!"

Mr. and Mrs. Lambchop were both very much in favor of politeness and careful speech. "Hay is for horses, Arthur, not people," Mr. Lambchop said as they entered the bedroom. "Try to remember that."

"Excuse me," Arthur said. "But look!"

He pointed to Stanley's bed. Across it lay the enormous bulletin board that Mr. Lambchop had given the boys a Christmas ago, so that they could pin up pictures and messages and maps. It had fallen, during the night, on top of Stanley.

But Stanley was not hurt. In fact, he would still have been sleeping if he had not been woken by his brother's shout. "What's going on here?" he called out cheerfully from beneath the enormous board.

Mr. and Mrs. Lambchop hurried to lift it from the bed.

"Heavens!" said Mrs. Lambchop.

"Gosh!" said Arthur. "Stanley's flat!"

374

"As a pancake," said Mr. Lambchop. "Darndest thing I've ever seen."

"Let's all have breakfast," Mrs. Lambchop said. "Then Stanley and I will go to see Doctor Dan and hear what he has to say."

The examination was almost over.

"How do you feel?" Doctor Dan asked. "Does it hurt very much?"

"I felt sort of tickly for a while after I got up," Stanley Lambchop said, "but I feel fine now."

"Well, that's mostly how it is with these cases," said Doctor Dan.

"We'll just have to keep an eye on this young fellow," he said when he had finished the examination. He told his nurse to take Stanley's measurements.

Mrs. Lambchop wrote them down.

Stanley was four feet tall, about a foot wide, and half an inch thick.

When Stanley got used to being flat, he enjoyed it. He could go in and out of rooms, even when the door was closed, just by lying down and sliding through the crack at the bottom.

Mr. and Mrs. Lambchop said it was silly, but they were quite proud of him. Arthur got jealous and tried to slide under a door, but he just banged his head.

Being flat could also be helpful, Stanley found. He was taking a walk with Mrs. Lambchop one afternoon when her favorite ring fell from her finger. The ring rolled across the sidewalk and down between the bars of a grating that covered a dark, deep shaft. Mrs. Lambchop began to cry.

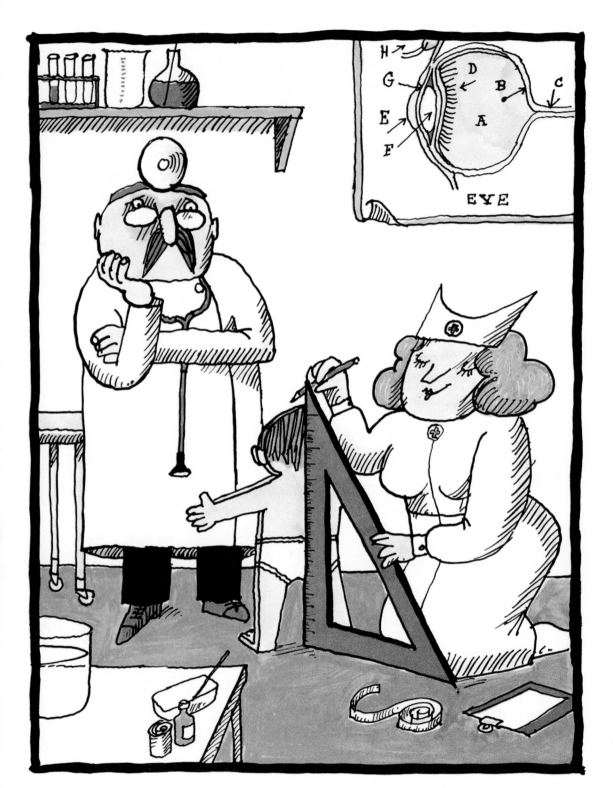

EYE

377

"I have an idea," Stanley said. He took the laces out of his shoes and an extra pair out of his pocket and tied them all together to make one long lace. Then he tied the end of that to the back of his belt and gave the other end to his mother. "Lower me," he said, "and I will look for the ring."

"Thank you, Stanley," Mrs. Lambchop said. She lowered him between the bars and moved him carefully up and down and from side to side, so that he could search the whole floor of the shaft.

Two policemen came by and stared at Mrs. Lambchop as she stood holding the long lace that ran down through the grating. She pretended not to notice them.

"What's the matter, lady?" the first policeman asked. "Is your yo-yo stuck?"

"I am not playing with a yo-yo!" Mrs. Lambchop said sharply. "My son is at the other end of this lace, if you must know."

"Get the net, Harry," said the second policeman. "We have caught a cuckoo!"

Just then, down in the shaft, Stanley cried out, "Hooray!"

Mrs. Lambchop pulled him up and saw that he had the ring.

"Good for you, Stanley," she said. Then she turned angrily to the policemen. "A cuckoo, indeed!" she said. "Shame!"

The policemen apologized. "We didn't get it, lady," they said. "We have been hasty. We see that now."

"People should think twice before making rude remarks," said Mrs. Lambchop. "And then not make them at all."

The policemen realized that was a good rule and said they would try to remember it.

379

One day Stanley got a letter from his friend Thomas Anthony Jeffrey, whose family had moved recently to California. A school vacation was about to begin, and Stanley was invited to spend it with the Jeffreys. "Oh, boy!" Stanley said. "I would love to go!"

Mr. Lambchop sighed. "A round-trip train or airplane ticket from New York to California is very expensive," he said. "I will have to think of some cheaper way."

When Mr. Lambchop came home from the office that evening, he brought with him an enormous brown paper envelope.

"Now then, Stanley," he said. "Try this for size."

The envelope fit Stanley very well. There was even room left over, Mrs. Lambchop discovered, for an egg-salad sandwich made with thin bread, and a flat cigarette case filled with milk. They had to put a great many stamps on the envelope to pay for both airmail and insurance, but it was still much less expensive than a train or airplane ticket to California would have been.

The next day Mr. and Mrs. Lambchop slid Stanley into his envelope, along with the egg-salad sandwich and the cigarette case full of milk, and mailed him from the box on the corner. The envelope had to be folded to fit through the slot. But Stanley was a limber boy and inside the box he straightened right up again.

Mrs. Lambchop was nervous because Stanley had never been away from home alone before. She rapped on the box. "Can you hear me, dear?" she called. "Are you all right?"

Stanley's voice came quite clearly. "I'm fine. Can I eat my sandwich now?"

"Wait an hour. And try not to get overheated, dear," Mrs. Lambchop said. Then she and Mr. Lambchop cried out, "Good-bye, good-bye!" and went home.

Stanley had a fine time in California. When the visit was over, the Jeffreys returned him in a beautiful white envelope they had made themselves. It had red and blue markings to show that it was airmail, and Thomas Jeffrey had lettered it "Valuable" and "Fragile" and "This End Up" on both sides.

Back home Stanley told his family that he had been handled so carefully he never felt a single bump. Mr. Lambchop said it proved that jet planes were wonderful, and so was the Post Office Department, and that this was a great age in which to live.

Stanley thought so too.

After a few more weeks, however, Stanley was no longer enjoying himself. People had begun to laugh and make fun of him as he passed by. "Hello, Super-Skinny!" they would shout, and even say ruder things about the way he looked.

Stanley told his parents how he felt. "It's the other kids I mostly mind," he said. "They don't like me any more because I'm different. Flat."

"Shame on them," Mrs. Lambchop said. "It is wrong to dislike people for their shapes. Or their religion, for that matter, or the color of their skin."

"I know," Stanley said. "Only maybe it's impossible for everybody to like *everybody*."

"Perhaps," said Mrs. Lambchop. "But they can try."

Later that night Arthur Lambchop was awakened by the sound of crying. In the darkness he crept across the room and knelt by Stanley's bed.

"Are you okay?" he said.

"Go away," Stanley said.

"Please let's be friends. . . ." Arthur couldn't help crying a little, too. "Oh, Stanley," he said. "Please tell me what's wrong."

Stanley waited for a long time before he spoke. "The thing is," he said, "I'm just not happy any more. I'm tired of being flat. I want to be a regular shape again, like other people. But I'll have to go on being flat forever. It makes me sick."

"Oh, Stanley," Arthur said. He dried his tears on a corner of Stanley's sheet and could think of nothing more to say.

"Don't talk about what I just said," Stanley told him. "I don't want the folks to worry. That would only make it worse."

"You're brave," Arthur said. "You really are."

He took hold of Stanley's hand. The two brothers sat together in the darkness, being friends. They were both still sad, but each one felt a *little* better than he had before.

And then, suddenly, though he was not even trying to think, Arthur had an idea. He jumped up and turned on the light and ran to the big storage box where toys and things were kept. He began to rummage in the box.

Stanley sat up in bed to watch.

382

Arthur flung aside a football and some lead soldiers

and airplane models and lots of wooden blocks, and then he said, "Aha!" He had found what he wanted—an old bicycle pump. He held it up, and Stanley and he looked at each other.

"Okay," Stanley said at last. "But take it easy." He put the end of the long pump hose in his mouth and clamped his lips tightly around it so that no air could escape.

"I'll go slowly," Arthur said. "If it hurts or anything, wiggle your hand at me."

He began to pump. At first nothing happened except that Stanley's cheeks bulged a bit. Arthur watched his hand, but there was no wiggle signal, so he pumped on. Then, suddenly, Stanley's top half began to swell.

"It's working! It's working!" shouted Arthur, pumping away.

Stanley spread his arms so that the air could get around inside him more easily. He got bigger and bigger. The buttons of his pajama top burst off—*Pop! Pop! Pop!* A moment more and he was all rounded out—head and body, arms and legs. But not his right foot. That foot stayed flat.

Arthur stopped pumping. "It's like trying to do the very last bit of those long balloons," he said. "Maybe a shake would help."

Stanley shook his right foot twice, and with a little *whooshing* sound it swelled out to match the left one. There stood Stanley Lambchop as he used to be, as if he had never been flat at all!

"Thank you, Arthur," Stanley said. "Thank you very much."

The brothers were shaking hands when Mr. Lambchop strode into the room with Mrs. Lambchop right behind him.

"We heard you!" said Mr. Lambchop. "Up and talking when you ought to be asleep, eh? Shame on—"

"GEORGE!" said Mrs. Lambchop. "Stanley's *round* again!"

"You're right!" said Mr. Lambchop, noticing. "Good for you, Stanley!"

"I'm the one who did it," Arthur said. "I blew him up."

Everyone was terribly excited and happy, of course. Mrs. Lambchop made hot chocolate to celebrate the occasion, and several toasts were drunk to Arthur for his cleverness.

When the little party was over, Mr. and Mrs. Lambchop tucked the boys back into their beds and kissed them, and then they turned out the light. "Good night," they said.

"Good night," said Stanley and Arthur.

It had been a long and tiring day. Very soon all the Lambchops were asleep.

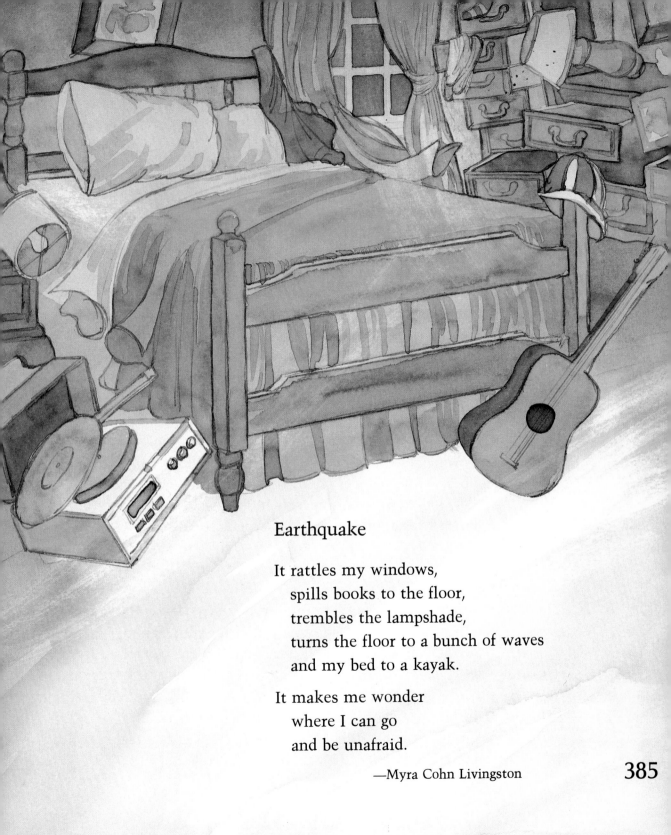

Earthquake

It rattles my windows,
   spills books to the floor,
   trembles the lampshade,
   turns the floor to a bunch of waves
   and my bed to a kayak.

It makes me wonder
   where I can go
   and be unafraid.

—Myra Cohn Livingston

385

Payday

BEVERLY CLEARY

"Ye-e-ep!" sang Ramona, as she printed *mice or ginny pig* on her Christmas list with purple crayon. Next to Christmas and her birthday, her father's payday was her favorite day. His payday meant treats. Her mother's payday from her part-time job in a doctor's office meant they could make payments on the bedroom the Quimbys had added to their house when Ramona was in first grade.

She wondered what the treat would be this payday. Maybe, since this was Friday, they could all go to a movie if her parents could find one suitable. Or maybe their father would bring presents, a package of colored paper for Ramona, a paperback book for Beezus.

"I wish I could think of something interesting to do with leftover pot roast and creamed cauliflower," remarked Mrs. Quimby.

Leftovers—yuck!, thought Ramona. "Maybe Daddy will take us to the Whopperburger for supper for payday," she said. A soft, juicy hamburger spiced with relish, French fries crisp on the outside and mealy inside, a little paper cup of coleslaw at the Whopperburger Restaurant were Ramona's favorite payday treat. Eating close together in a booth made Ramona feel snug and cozy. She and Beezus never quarreled at the Whopperburger.

"Good idea." Mrs. Quimby closed the refrigerator door. "I'll see what I can do."

Ramona had decided to order a cheeseburger when she heard the sound of her father's key in the front door. "Daddy, Daddy!" she shrieked, scrambling down from the chair and running to meet her father as he opened the door. "Guess what?"

Beezus, who had come from her room, answered before her father had a chance to guess. "Mother said maybe we could go to the Whopperburger for dinner!"

Mr. Quimby smiled and kissed his daughters before he held out a small, white, paper bag. "Here, I brought you a little present." Somehow he did not look as happy as usual. Maybe he had had a hard day at the office of the moving-and-storage company where he worked.

His daughters pounced and opened the bag together. "Gummybears!" was their joyful cry. The chewy little bears were the most popular sweet at Glenwood School this fall. Last spring powdered Jell-O eaten from the package had been the fad. Mr. Quimby always remembered these things.

"Run along and divide them between you," said Mr. Quimby. "I want to talk to your mother."

"Don't spoil your dinner," said Mrs. Quimby.

The girls bore the bag off to Beezus's room, where they dumped the gummybears onto the bedspread. First they divided the cinnamon-flavored red bears, one for Beezus, one for Ramona. Then they divided the orange bears and the green, and as they were about to divide the yellow bears, both girls were suddenly aware that their mother and father were no longer talking. Silence filled the house. The sisters looked at one another. There was

387

something unnatural about this silence. Uneasy, they waited for some sound, and then their parents began to speak in whispers. Beezus tiptoed to the door to listen.

Ramona bit the head off a red gummybear. She always ate toes last. "Maybe they're planning a big surprise," she suggested, refusing to worry.

"I don't think so," whispered Beezus, "but I can't hear what they are saying."

"Try listening through the furnace pipes," whispered Ramona.

"That won't work here. The living room is too far away." Beezus strained to catch her parents' words. "I think something's wrong."

Ramona divided her gummybears, one heap to eat at home, the other to take to school to share with friends if they were nice to her.

"Something is wrong. Something awful," whispered Beezus. "I can tell by the way they're talking."

Beezus looked so frightened that Ramona became frightened too. What could be wrong? She tried to think what she might have done to make her parents whisper this way, but she had stayed out of trouble lately. She could not think of a single thing that could be wrong. This frightened her even more. She no longer felt like eating chewy little bears. She wanted to know why her mother and father were whispering in a way that alarmed Beezus.

Finally the girls heard their father say in a normal voice, "I think I'll take a shower before supper." This remark was reassuring to Ramona.

"What'll we do now?" whispered Beezus. "I'm scared to go out."

Worry and curiosity, however, urged Beezus and Ramona into the hall.

Trying to pretend they were not concerned about their family, the girls walked into the kitchen where Mrs. Quimby was removing leftovers from the refrigerator. "I think we'll eat at home after all," she said, looking sad and anxious.

Without being asked, Ramona began to deal four place mats around the dining-room table, laying them all right side up. When she was cross with Beezus, she laid her sister's place mat face down.

Mrs. Quimby looked at the cold creamed cauliflower with distaste, returned it to the refrigerator, and reached for a can of green beans before she noticed her silent and worried daughters watching her for clues as to what might be wrong.

Mrs. Quimby turned and faced Beezus and Ramona. "Girls, you might as well know. Your father has lost his job."

"But he liked his job," said Ramona, regretting the loss of that hamburger and those French fries eaten in the coziness of a booth. She had known her father to change jobs because he had not liked his work, but she had never heard of him losing a job.

"Was he fired?" asked Beezus, shocked at the news.

Mrs. Quimby opened the green beans and dumped them into a saucepan before she explained. "Losing his job was not your father's fault. He worked for a little company. A big company bought the little company and let out most of the people who worked for the little company."

"But we won't have enough money." Beezus understood these things better than Ramona.

"Mother works," Ramona reminded her sister.

"Only part time," said Mrs. Quimby. "And we have to make payments to the bank for the new room. That's why I went to work."

"What will we do?" asked Ramona, alarmed at last. Would they go hungry? Would the men from the bank come and tear down the new room if they couldn't pay for it? She had never thought what it might be like not to have enough money—not that the Quimbys ever had money to spare. Although Ramona had often heard her mother say that house payments, car payments, taxes, and groceries seemed to eat up money, the Quimbys somehow managed to make their money pay for all they really needed, with a little treat now and then besides.

"We will have to manage as best we can until your

father finds work," said Mrs. Quimby. "It might not be easy."

"Maybe I could baby-sit," volunteered Beezus.

As she laid out knives and forks, Ramona wondered how she could earn money too. She could have a lemonade stand in front of the house, except nobody ever bought lemonade but her father and her friend Howie. She thought about pounding rose petals and soaking them in water to make perfume to sell. Unfortunately, the perfume she tried to make always smelled like rotten rose petals, and anyway the roses were almost gone.

"And girls," said Mrs. Quimby, lowering her voice as if she was about to share a secret, "you mustn't do anything to annoy your father. He is worried enough right now."

But he remembered to bring gummybears, thought Ramona, who never wanted to annoy her father or her mother either, just Beezus, although sometimes, without even trying, she succeeded in annoying her whole family. Ramona felt sad and somehow lonely, as if she were left out of something important, because her family was in trouble and there was nothing she could do to help. When she had finished setting the table, she returned to the list she had begun, it now seemed, a long time ago. "But what about Christmas?" she asked her mother.

"Right now Christmas is the least of our worries." Mrs. Quimby looked sadder than Ramona had ever seen her look. "Taxes are due in November. And we have to buy groceries and make car payments and a lot of other things."

"Don't we have any money in the bank?" asked Beezus.

"Not much," admitted Mrs. Quimby, "but your father was given two weeks pay."

Ramona looked at the list she had begun so happily and wondered how much the presents she had listed would cost. Too much, she knew. Mice were free if you knew the right person, the owner of a mother mouse, so she might get some mice.

Slowly Ramona crossed out *ginny pig* and the other presents she had listed. As she made black lines through each item, she thought about her family. She did not want her father to be worried, her mother sad, or her sister cross. She wanted her whole family, including their cat, Picky-picky, to be happy.

Ramona studied her crayons, chose a pinky red one because it seemed the happiest color, and printed one more item on her Christmas list to make up for all she had crossed out. *One happy family*. Beside the words she drew four smiling faces and beside them the face of a yellow cat, also smiling.

Unit Nine
Pastimes

Bowl Game

ROBERT HOFSINDE

The rain was pelting down on the skin covering of the tepee. A group of Crow Indians sat snug within, playing the bowl game around a small fire made of buffalo chips.

One player held a small wooden bowl in his hand. As the others looked on, he tossed into the air a number of peach pits that were in the bowl. Then he skillfully caught them in the bowl again.

The players were divided into two teams. Both teams watched closely to see how the stones landed and how the play was scored. Both sides wanted to win, for each player on the winning side would be given a pony by the losers.

To play the game with your friends, you need the following equipment:

> *One small unbreakable bowl or basket*
> *Six peach or plum pits, or six small stones*
> *A felt tipped pen or marker*

Any even number of people can play this game, even as few as two. It is more exciting if there are three or four players, or even more, on each team.

First, wash the fruit pits and let them dry thoroughly. Then draw a broad line with the pen across one side of each pit or stone, as shown.

Drop the six pits into the bowl or basket. Hold the bowl in one hand and, with a slight toss, flip the pits up into the air and catch them again in the bowl. Score by

394

counting the number of pits that land with the marked side up. Each one that lands with the marked side up counts one point.

After scoring your turn, pass the bowl over to your opponent. He or she makes a toss, counts the score, and passes the bowl to the next player.

Each player keeps her or his own score with toothpicks. The winner is the one having the most toothpicks after twenty tosses.

If as many as six are playing the game, divide up into two teams, facing each other, with three players on each team. The first player on your team makes the first toss and counts the score. Then the bowl is passed to the opponent directly opposite. The opponent tosses, counts the score, and passes the bowl to the second player on your team.

Although each player usually keeps his or her own score, an official scorekeeper may be appointed. At the end of a game of ten tosses by each player, the final team scores are tallied, and the team with the larger score wins.

Some form of this bowl game was played by nearly every tribe of Native Americans in the country. The Plains and Woodland Indians used a wooden bowl for the game. The Indians of the Southwest more often used a fine, woven basket.

Atalanta and Hippomenes

MARGARET EVANS PRICE

Atalanta was a Greek maiden who could run faster than any one on earth. She could outrun the winds, Boreas and Zephyr. Only Mercury, with his winged sandals, ran more swiftly.

Besides being so fleet-footed, Atalanta was very beautiful, and many Greek youths from every part of the kingdom wished to marry her. But Atalanta did not wish to marry any one and turned them all away, saying, "I shall be the bride only of him who shall outrun me in the race. Death must be the penalty of all who try and fail."

In spite of this hard condition there still were a few brave suitors willing to risk their lives for a chance of winning Atalanta.

For one of the races the runners chose the youth Hippomenes for judge. Hippomenes felt both pity and scorn for the runners. He thought they were foolish to risk their lives, and told them to go home. He reminded them that the land was full of lovely maidens who were kinder and more gentle than Atalanta.

"But you have not yet seen Atalanta," said one of the suitors to Hippomenes. "You do not know all her beauty and loveliness. See, she comes!"

Hippomenes looked, and saw Atalanta as she drew near. She laid aside her cloak and made ready for the race. For a moment she stood poised like a graceful bird about to fly.

At a word from Hippomenes the runners were off, but at the first step Atalanta flew ahead. Her tunic fluttered behind her like a banner. Her hair blew about her shoulders in bright waves.

As she ran, Hippomenes thought her very beautiful and became envious of the runner who might win her. He shouted praises when she reached the goal far ahead of her poor suitors.

Hippomenes forgot that the penalty of failure was death. He did not remember the advice he had given the other runners to go home and forget the loveliness of Atalanta. He knew only that he loved her and must himself race with her. So the race was arranged for a few days later.

398

Raising his head toward Mount Olympus, Hippomenes prayed to Venus, the goddess of love, and asked her to help him.

As he stood beside Atalanta, waiting the signal for the race to start, Venus appeared to him and slipped three golden apples into his hands. "Throw them one by one in Atalanta's path," she whispered.

The goddess was invisible to everyone but Hippomenes. No one saw her as she gave him the apples, nor heard her as she told him what to do with them.

Atalanta looked pityingly at the handsome youth as he stood ready to run. She was sorry for him, and for a moment she hesitated and almost wished that he might win the race.

The signal was given, and Atalanta and Hippomenes flew swiftly over the sand. Atalanta was soon ahead, but Hippomenes, sending up a prayer to Venus, tossed one of his

399

golden apples so that it fell directly in front of Atalanta. Astonished at the beautiful apple which seemed to fall from nowhere, she stooped to pick it up.

That instant Hippomenes passed her. But Atalanta, holding the apple firmly in her hand, at once darted ahead. Again she outdistanced Hippomenes. Then he threw the second apple.

Atalanta could not pass without picking it up, and then, because of the apple in her other hand, paused a moment longer. When she looked up, Hippomenes was far ahead. But gaining, she overtook and passed him. Then, just before she reached the goal, he threw the third apple.

"I can win easily," thought Atalanta, "even though I stoop for this other apple." As she was already holding an apple in each hand, she paused just for an instant as she wondered how to grasp the third.

At that moment Hippomenes shot past, reaching the goal before Atalanta.

Upon hearing the wild shouts of those who watched, Atalanta realized that she had let herself be tricked, and smiled ruefully at Hippomenes.

Contest Fever

DALE FIFE

News spread fast on Plum Street. Soon almost everyone knew about Lincoln's contest fever.

Every time Officer Roberts saw Lincoln he asked him if he'd won anything yet. Harry, the postman, began shaking his head as soon as he saw Lincoln waiting hopefully by the mailbox.

Bunky made another sign for the clubhouse. It was bigger than he was. He brought it to Lincoln for a look. Under the words THE PLUM STREET ATHLETIC CLUB, he had drawn a basketball, a football, a baseball and bat, a Ping-Pong table, a TV, a big desk, and four easy chairs.

"What's all that mean?" Lincoln asked.

"It's the inside of our clubhouse," Bunky said.

"Great!" Lincoln said. "But we haven't got any of those things. All we've got is the promise of a basketball from Uncle Jay."

"We will have when your prizes come," Bunky said confidently.

And then they did. That very day when the postman came, he had a letter for Lincoln. He handed him the long white envelope, edged in red and blue, and then, grinning, waited for Lincoln to open it.

Lincoln let out a shout that brought his sisters Sissy and Sassy from the kitchen, Wilbur from across the hall, and Bunky from the stoop outside. "It's from the Hiram Soup Company," Lincoln said, hypnotized by his first airmail letter.

"Open it, you dope," Wilbur said.

Lincoln felt sort of frozen outside and quivery like jelly inside as he tore open the envelope and pulled out the letter. It was short. Four lines. He read, "We are pleased to advise you that you are a winner in the Hiram's Soup contest. Your prize will be delivered in a few days."

The letter was signed by the president of the company, whose name wasn't Hiram at all, but Jason Winkler, Jr.

Everyone was excited. The twins hugged him. Bunky's eyes were wide with hero worship. "From now on you're Lucky Lincoln," Wilbur said.

Success! It was sweet. It made everything different. Unreal. It seemed to Lincoln that his feet didn't touch the floor, and his head floated up around the ceiling somewhere.

Bunky ran around in circles shouting, "We've got a color TV for our clubhouse . . . we've got a color TV . . ."

Sassy outshouted him. "What do you mean for the clubhouse? We'll use it right here at home."

"Yes," Sissy said. "Lincoln can take our old black and white set to the clubhouse. The picture's pretty awful anyhow."

Bunky stuck out his chin. "I own ten percent of the prize. My part goes to the clubhouse."

"What's your part?" Sassy asked.

"The aerial," Bunky said.

The argument raged, but Lincoln was above such petty squabbling. Half an hour ago he had been just plain Lincoln. Now he was Lucky Lincoln. A winner. Like a star athlete hoisted on the shoulders of his teammates. He, Lucky Lincoln, would keep right on winning until he was the biggest contest star in New York City. Maybe in the whole country.

"Stop arguing," he said, from his heady elevation. "I'll probably win another color TV tomorrow. The first one goes to the clubhouse."

That silenced everyone. Lucky Lincoln, the winner, had spoken.

Lincoln's prize arrived two days later. When he came home from school with Wilbur, Bunky was waiting for him. "The TV is here," he cried. "It just came."

Sissy and Sassy were at the open window. "Hurry, we can hardly wait," Sassy yelled.

The boys rushed into the apartment. A big box stood in the middle of the living room. Lincoln got a knife from the kitchen and slashed it open. A notice in bold letters lay on the top. It read:

CONGRATULATIONS

We are sure you will be delighted with your prize in

HIRAM'S SOUP CONTEST—

12 dozen cans of Hiram's mouth-watering soup!

The blow stunned Lincoln speechless.

Bunky stuck his head in the box. "You mean we don't get a color TV for the clubhouse?"

Sassy took a handful of the shredded paper from around the cans, wadded it into a ring, and stuck it on Lincoln's head. "Hail, the Soup King of Plum Street."

"Cheer up," Sissy said. "It's better to have a booby prize than no prize at all."

"Aw, slice it off," Lincoln said. "So I didn't get first today. I probably will tomorrow."

Now the postman had mail for Lincoln. And packages. Lincoln didn't win the clock-radio in the Magic Shaving Cream contest, but he did get a year's supply of shaving cream.

He didn't get the electric guitar for his name "Astrostars" in the Name the Cookie contest, but he did get a cookbook.

He missed out on the Ping-Pong table in the Count the Rabbits in the Cabbage Patch contest, but he won one hundred balloons. Not all blown up, of course, but deflated and neatly packed in a box.

Lincoln won a birdhouse, but he didn't have a tree to hang it in. He lost out on the barbells in the Name the Buffalo contest, but he did win twelve skiing lessons in Idaho.

Of course, there were contests he didn't hear from, and there were contests where everyone who entered won a prize, and sometimes it was something silly like a plastic ring with fake rubies. His room was cluttered with booby prizes. There were measuring cups and key chains, watch charms and pencil sharpeners. A kite hung from the ceiling. Cartons were under his bed and piled up against the wall. Shredded paper littered the rug.

One Saturday his sister Sara said, "Going into your room is as dangerous as crossing Broadway at Forty-second Street. You'll just have to find some other place to put all this junk."

"Where?" Lincoln asked. "I gave Mom as much soup and soap as she could get into her cupboard. Pop said two tubes of shaving cream would last him until New Year's."

"Well, you'd better find a way to get rid of it. It's about time for Grandpa's visit, and he always shares your room."

Lincoln was still thinking about it a week later when Sara again tackled his room. This time she really blew.

405

Mom came hurrying into Lincoln's room, all ready to go to a meeting. She looked around. Then she gave a "no fooling" order. "I want to find your room cleared out when I get back. Give these things away or take them around the corner to the junkman. Don't waste any time. He closes at noon on Saturday."

"I'll get only about one cent a pound," Lincoln wailed.

But no one listened.

Lincoln looked around at all his prizes. He had got used to having them in his room. While they were around, he had some hope that the next package would be something worthwhile.

He went outside and sat on the steps, feeling glummer than glum. Bunky came along. He had a new entry blank. It was for a canned spinach contest. "Look, Link, this is the best kind. You don't have to do a thing but write your name and address. The first prize is an automobile. Wouldn't it be neat if the Plum Street Athletic Club had its own automobile?"

"What's the booby prize, Bunk?"

"They're giving away a hundred thousand nifty can openers."

"That's just what I need, one hundred thousand can openers to get into my room," Lincoln said, handing the blank to Bunky. "Why don't you try it?"

"Me? You're the lucky one. I can't even write good."

Sara came out of the apartment. "Mom meant it about your room," she said, as she started down the street.

Meanwhile, Fats Butch was walking up the street toward the drugstore. He stopped in front of Lincoln and Bunky to scratch himself.

"He's got fleas," Bunky said.

"Yeah, he's a regular flea bag. Why, he's got so many fleas he could open a flea market . . . *Flea Market!* . . . *FLEA MARKET!*"

Lincoln jumped to his feet. "Bunky, I've got an idea. We're going to have a flea market."

"You mean we're going to hop around like fleas on a dog's back?" Bunky asked.

"No, I mean we're going to have a sale. I can get rid of all that junk in my room, and we'll get money for the clubhouse."

"That's a great idea!" said Bunky. "I knew your prizes would make our clubhouse look great."

Bedtime

Five minutes, five minutes more, please!
  Let me stay five minutes more!
Can't I just finish the castle
  I'm building here on the floor?
Can't I just finish the story
  I'm reading here in my book?
Can't I just finish this bead-chain—
  It *almost* is finished, look!
Can't I just finish this game, please?
  When a game's once begun
It's a pity never to find out
  Whether you've lost or won.
Can't I just stay five minutes?
  Well, can't I stay just four?
Three minutes, then? two minutes?
  Can't I stay *one* minute more?

—Eleanor Farjeon

Parties and Pastimes in the Old West

RUSSELL FREEDMAN

When pioneer children finished their chores, they had the wide open spaces as their playground. They explored creek beds with their dogs, hiked to the top of sun-parched hills, raced across dusty fields on their ponies, and spent long summer days at the local swimming hole.

Sarah Bixby remembered her childhood summers on a California ranch during the 1870s:

"We could go down to the orchard, where all summer long there were ripe apples and pears, or we could shed our shoes and wade in the San Gabriel River. . . . We could watch hundreds of pigeons flying in and out of the deserted adobe ranch house, known to us, because of its condition, as 'The Flea House.' Or we could go to our retreat in an enlarged coyote hole in the pasture on the other side of the hill. Luckily we did not find any rattlesnakes sharing it with us. We could play in the old stagecoach left in the weeds outside the fence. It remained from earlier days, when it carried the mails, express, and passengers between San Diego, Los Angeles, and San Francisco."

A birthday party at a Colorado ranch

On weekends and holidays, pioneer families relaxed at church socials, community dances, and neighborly house parties. They gathered for picnics in the churchyard or in some shady grove beside a creek. Each family brought baskets and buckets heaped with food. Often they barbecued fresh pork or buffalo meat over open fires. After lunch, children jumped rope, played tag, and flew homemade kites. Everyone joined in songfests, ball games, and foot races.

409

A lawn party in Orofino, Idaho

    Dancing was a favorite pastime among youngsters and grown-ups alike. At housewarmings, weddings, and holiday celebrations, settlers decked out in their Sunday best enjoyed round after round of polkas, waltzes, and square dances. Special community dances might be held almost anywhere—on a big, outdoor platform, in the local schoolhouse or courthouse, or in a livery stable that had been cleared and decorated for the occasion. Everyone went to these affairs—small children, young couples, parents, and grandparents. A local fiddler played the popular tunes of the day. Folks on the sidelines clapped their hands and tapped their feet as a caller led the dancers through their steps: "Swing an' march—first couple lead, clear 'round the hall and then stampede!"

Children always looked forward to spending a Saturday afternoon in town. The main street was crowded with suspendered men and sun-bonneted women from outlying homesteads, and with fancy visitors from the East. Cowboys wearing boots and spurs swaggered down the wooden sidewalks. Indians wrapped in blankets traded at the general store. At the stage depot, youngsters watched coaches swing out for some distant city and wondered whether the passengers would have a safe trip. Sometimes a photographer passed through town, using his wagon as a studio. He would set up his big, boxlike camera and invite settlers to stand and pose as he captured the images we see today.

Nearly every frontier town was visited by the entertainers that traveled back and forth through the West. Magicians, jugglers, snake charmers, and sword swallowers performed before coin-tossing crowds in the town square. No town was too small to attract the traveling peddlers who carried suitcases filled with patent medicines. People would gather as the golden-voiced medicine man set up shop in some weed-grown, empty lot. After bringing the crowd under his spell, he would unpack his miraculous wares: Hamlin's Wizard Oil, Dr. John Bull's Vegetable Worm Destroyer, Dr. B.P. Sherman's Pricklyrash Bitters. Sometimes he convinced his listeners that his medicines really worked, and always he entertained them.

Most towns had a theater where professional troupes performed everything from slapstick comedies to tear-jerking melodramas. Enthusiastic audiences shouted warnings, advice, and encouragement to the actors. Shakespeare's plays were so popular in the West that many theatergoers knew the lines by heart and were not afraid to yell them out if an actor hesitated. Even small communities without professional theaters had amateur theatrical groups that performed in schoolhouses and town halls.

Every summer, at least one traveling circus would roll into town. Children flocked from miles around to watch the circus parade down the main street with its brass bands, tumbling clowns, prancing horses, marching elephants, whistling calliopes, and wagon after wagon of wild animals growling and roaring in their cages. Youngsters ran alongside and followed the parade to the outskirts of town, where they watched and sometimes helped the circus workers put up the big tent and unload the animals. These frontier circuses were not so different from the ones we have today. In an age when movies and television were unknown, they had no competition as "The Greatest Show on Earth."

A circus parade marches down the main street of Salida, Colorado.

Christmas toys. Store-bought toys like these were a luxury on the frontier. Most children received simple homemade gifts.

Another pleasure of a frontier childhood was celebrating Christmas. If a family lived near a stand of evergreens, they would pick out a tree, chop it down, and carry it home. The tree was decorated with strings of cranberries and popcorn, colored ribbons, paper cutouts, and candy apples. Candle holders cut from tin were fastened to the branches. Sometimes there were little wooden animals and people, drums, and boxes, all of them carved and painted by hand.

On Christmas Eve, the smells of freshly made cakes, cookies, and candies drifted through the house. Long, red stockings by the fireplace were stuffed with Christmas taffy and gingersnaps, and with gifts for each child. Friends and neighbors shared a festive holiday dinner. Afterwards they recited Christmas poems and prayers and sang traditional carols as the fireplace glowed and the candles flickered on the tree.

Christmas was a time for families and friends to celebrate at home. The Fourth of July was a community event, celebrated by the whole town. It was the one day of the year when everyone who could possibly make it headed for town to join the festivities. A notice might be posted:

A great 4th of July at Douglass [Kansas] 1871. Everybody is invited to come and bring filled baskets and buckets. There will be a famous speaker present, who will tell of the big future in store for southern Kansas. Grand fireworks at night! Eighteen dollars worth of sky rockets and other brilliant blazes will light up the night! There will also be a bunch of Osage Indians and cowboys to help make the program interesting. After the fireworks there will be a big platform dance, with music by the Hatfield Brothers.

At sunrise on the Fourth, a cannon was fired in the town square. If the town had no cannon, gunpowder was exploded on a blacksmith's anvil. These salutes could be heard for miles. Children in outlying homesteads would get up before dawn and listen closely as the sounds of the explosions reached them, first from one direction, then from another.

When the morning chores were finished and an early breakfast gulped down, families packed their picnic baskets, hitched up their teams, and drove into town. Wagons and buggies were decorated with red, white, and blue bunting. Little flags flew from the horses' bridles.

The day's activities might be held in the town square, on the main street, or in a wooded grove outside of town.

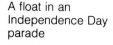

A float in an Independence Day parade

Leading citizens delivered patriotic speeches and read from the Declaration of Independence. There was always a big parade led by the town band. Caught up in the spirit of the day, settlers cheered and applauded as the marchers passed by. Children marched along to the beat of the fife-and-drum corps.

After the parade, the settlers would feast on their picnic lunches. Then they joined in games and sports that went on all afternoon. There were foot races, horse races, sack races, and wagon races; ball games and pie-eating contests. Boys and men tried to climb greased poles or catch oiled pigs.

In the evening, fireworks lit up the sky. The day was rounded out by a community dance held on an outdoor platform by the glow of lanterns.

Many of the children who took part in these celebrations had traveled west with wagon trains. All of them had helped settle the frontier. They had faced dangers and overcome hardships that we today can only faintly imagine. It is hardly surprising that these youngsters felt proud of themselves, their communities, and their country. They would remember those Fourth of July celebrations for the rest of their lives.

Harriet Walker recalled:

How our hearts thrilled as we heard the military band which played the patriotic airs. . . . At eleven o'clock there was a parade led by the flag bearer and band. Then there was a float filled with as many little girls as we had states, little girls dressed in white with sashes and caps of red, white, and blue, representing each state of the Union. In front holding the flag was the loveliest being on earth—the Goddess of Liberty—dressed in white, a silver starry crown on her head, and her long hair waving in the breeze. They sang 'America' and the 'Star Spangled Banner.' Do you wonder then that our hearts were thrilled, and that we were proud of our country, and our hearts were filled with patriotism?

415

Rope Rhyme

Get set, ready now, jump right in
Bounce and kick and giggle and spin
Listen to the rope when it hits the ground
Listen to that clappedy-slappedy sound
Jump right up when it tells you to
Come back down, whatever you do
Count to a hundred, count by ten
Start to count all over again
That's what jumping is all about
Get set, ready now,
    jump
        right
            out!

—Eloise Greenfield

416

A Mad Tea Party

LEWIS CARROLL

Alice, a girl about your age, has fallen down a rabbit hole and into a strange underground world. In this chapter from *Alice's Adventures in Wonderland,* she finds herself at a very unusual party.

There was a table set out under a tree in front of the house, and the March Hare and the Hatter were having tea at it. A Dormouse was sitting between them, fast asleep, and the other two were using it as a cushion, resting their elbows on it, and talking over its head. "Very uncomfortable for the Dormouse," thought Alice. "Only as it's asleep, I suppose it doesn't mind."

The table was a large one, but the three were all crowded together at one corner of it. "No room! No room!" they cried out when they saw Alice coming. "There's *plenty* of room!" said Alice indignantly, and she sat down in a large armchair at one end of the table.

"Have some wine," the March Hare said in an encouraging tone.

Alice looked all around the table, but there was nothing on it but tea. "I don't see any wine," she remarked.

"There isn't any," said the March Hare.

"Then it wasn't very civil of you to offer it," said Alice angrily.

"It wasn't very civil of you to sit down without being invited," said the March Hare.

417

"I didn't know it was *your* table," said Alice. "It's set for a great many more than three."

"Your hair needs cutting," said the Hatter. He had been looking at Alice for some time with great curiosity, and this was his first speech.

"You should learn not to make personal remarks," Alice said with some severity. "It's very rude."

The Hatter opened his eyes very wide on hearing this, but all he *said* was, "Why is a raven like a writing desk?"

"Come, we shall have some fun now!" thought Alice. "I'm glad they've begun asking riddles—I believe I can guess that," she added aloud.

"Do you mean that you think you can find out the answer to it?" said the March Hare.

"Exactly so," said Alice.

"Then you should say what you mean," the March Hare went on.

"I do," Alice hastily replied, "at least—at least I mean what I say—that's the same thing, you know."

"Not the same thing a bit!" said the Hatter. "Why, you might just as well say that 'I see what I eat' is the same thing as 'I eat what I see'!"

"You might just as well say," added the March Hare, "that 'I like what I get' is the same thing as 'I get what I like'!"

"You might just as well say," added the Dormouse, which seemed to be talking in its sleep, "that 'I breathe when I sleep' is the same thing as 'I sleep when I breathe'!"

"It *is* the same thing with you," said the Hatter, and here the conversation dropped. The party sat silent for a minute, while Alice thought over all she could remember about ravens and writing desks, which wasn't much.

The Hatter was the first to break the silence. "What day of the month is it?" he said, turning to Alice. He had taken his watch out of his pocket, and was looking at it uneasily, shaking it every now and then, and holding it to his ear.

Alice considered a little, and then said, "The fourth."

"Two days wrong!" sighed the Hatter. "I told you butter wouldn't suit the works!" he added, looking angrily at the March Hare.

"It was the *best* butter," the March Hare meekly replied.

"Yes, but some crumbs must have got in as well," the Hatter grumbled. "You shouldn't have put it in with the bread-knife."

The March Hare took the watch and looked at it gloomily. Then he dipped it into his cup of tea, and looked at it again. But he could think of nothing better to say than his first remark, "It was the *best* butter, you know."

Alice had been looking over his shoulder with some curiosity. "What a funny watch!" she remarked. "It tells the day of the month, and doesn't tell what time it is!"

"Why should it?" muttered the Hatter. "Does *your* watch tell you what year it is?"

"Of course not," Alice replied very readily. "But that's because it stays the same year for such a long time together."

"Which is just the case with *mine*," said the Hatter.

Alice felt dreadfully puzzled. The Hatter's remark seemed to her to have no sort of meaning in it, and yet it was certainly English. "I don't quite understand you," she said, as politely as she could.

"The Dormouse is asleep again," said the Hatter, and he poured a little hot tea upon its nose.

The Dormouse shook its head impatiently, and said,

420

without opening its eyes, "Of course, of course, just what I was going to remark myself."

"Have you guessed the riddle yet?" the Hatter said, turning to Alice again.

"No, I give it up," Alice replied. "What's the answer?"

"I haven't the slightest idea," said the Hatter.

"Nor I," said the March Hare.

Alice sighed wearily. "I think you might do something better with the time," she said, "than wasting it in asking riddles that have no answers."

"If you knew Time as well as I do," said the Hatter, "you wouldn't talk about wasting *it*. It's *him*."

"I don't know what you mean," said Alice.

"Of course you don't!" the Hatter said, tossing his head contemptuously. "I dare say you never even spoke to Time!"

"Perhaps not," Alice cautiously replied, "but I know I have to beat time when I learn music."

"Ah! That accounts for it," said the Hatter. "He won't stand beating. Now, if you only kept on good terms with him, he'd do almost anything you liked with the clock. For instance, suppose it were nine o'clock in the morning, just time to begin lessons. You'd only have to whisper a hint to

Time, and round goes the clock in a twinkling! Half-past one, time for dinner!"

("I only wish it was," the March Hare said to itself in a whisper.)

"That would be grand, certainly," said Alice thoughtfully. "But then—I shouldn't be hungry for it, you know."

"Not at first, perhaps," said the Hatter. "But you could keep it to half-past one as long as you liked."

"Is that the way *you* manage?" Alice asked.

The Hatter shook his head mournfully. "Not I!" he replied. "We quarreled last March—just before *he* went mad, you know—" (pointing with his teaspoon at the March Hare) "—it was at the great concert given by the Queen of Hearts, and I had to sing—

> 'Twinkle, twinkle, little bat!
> How I wonder what you're at!'

You know the song, perhaps?"

"I've heard something like it," said Alice.

"It goes on, you know," the Hatter continued, "in this way—

> 'Up above the world you fly,
> Like a tea tray in the sky.
> Twinkle, twinkle—' "

Here the Dormouse shook itself, and began singing in its sleep, "*Twinkle, twinkle, twinkle, twinkle*—" and went on so long that they had to pinch it to make it stop.

"Well, I'd hardly finished the first verse," said the Hatter, "when the Queen bawled out, 'He's murdering the time! Off with his head!' "

"How dreadfully savage!" exclaimed Alice.

"And ever since that," the Hatter went on in a mournful tone, "he won't do a thing I ask! It's always six o'clock now."

A bright idea came into Alice's head. "Is that the reason so many tea things are put out here?" she asked.

"Yes, that's it," said the Hatter with a sigh. "It's always teatime, and we've no time to wash the things between whiles."

"Then you keep moving round, I suppose?" said Alice.

"Exactly so," said the Hatter, "as the things get used up."

"But what happens when you come to the beginning again?" Alice ventured to ask.

"Suppose we change the subject," the March Hare interrupted, yawning. "I'm getting tired of this. I vote the young lady tells us a story."

"I'm afraid I don't know one," said Alice, rather alarmed at the proposal.

"Then the Dormouse shall!" they both cried. "Wake up, Dormouse!" And they pinched it on both sides at once.

The Dormouse slowly opened its eyes. "I wasn't asleep," it said in a hoarse, feeble voice. "I heard every word you fellows were saying."

"Tell us a story!" said the March Hare.

"Yes, please do!" pleaded Alice.

"And be quick about it," added the Hatter, "or you'll be asleep again before it's done."

"Once upon a time there were three little sisters," the Dormouse began in a great hurry, "and their names were Elsie, Lacie, and Tillie, and they lived at the bottom of a well—"

"What did they live on?" said Alice, who always took a great interest in questions of eating and drinking.

"They lived on treacle," said the Dormouse, after thinking a minute or two.

"They couldn't have done that, you know," Alice gently remarked. "They'd have been ill."

"So they were," said the Dormouse, "*very* ill."

Alice tried a little to fancy to herself what such an extraordinary way of living would be like, but it puzzled her too much. So she went on, "But why did they live at the bottom of a well?"

"Take some more tea," the March Hare said to Alice, very earnestly.

"I've had nothing yet," Alice replied in an offended tone, "so I can't take more."

"You mean you can't take *less*," said the Hatter: "it's very easy to take *more* than nothing."

"Nobody asked *your* opinion," said Alice.

"Who's making personal remarks now?" the Hatter asked triumphantly.

Alice did not quite know what to say to this. So she helped herself to some tea and bread and butter, and then turned to the Dormouse, and repeated her question. "Why did they live at the bottom of a well?"

The Dormouse again took a minute or two to think about it, and then said, "It was a treacle well."

"There's no such thing!" Alice was beginning very angrily, but the Hatter and the March Hare went, "Sh! Sh!" and the Dormouse sulkily remarked, "If you can't be civil, you'd better finish the story for yourself."

"No, please go on!" Alice said very humbly. "I won't interrupt you again. I dare say there may be *one*."

"One, indeed!" said the Dormouse indignantly. However, he consented to go on. "And so these three little

425

sisters—they were learning to draw, you know—"

"What did they draw?" said Alice, quite forgetting her promise.

"Treacle," said the Dormouse, without considering at all this time.

"I want a clean cup," interrupted the Hatter. "Let's all move one place on."

He moved on as he spoke, and the Dormouse followed him. The March Hare moved into the Dormouse's place, and Alice rather unwillingly took the place of the March Hare. The Hatter was the only one who got any advantage from the change, and Alice was a good deal worse off than before, as the March Hare had just upset the milk jug into his plate.

Alice did not wish to offend the Dormouse again, so she began very cautiously, "But I don't understand. Where did they draw the treacle from?"

"You can draw water out of a water well," said the Hatter, "so I should think you could draw treacle out of a treacle well—eh, stupid?"

"But they were *in* the well," Alice said to the Dormouse, not choosing to notice this last remark.

"Of course they were," said the Dormouse. "Well in."

This answer so confused poor Alice that she let the Dormouse go on for some time without interrupting it.

"They were learning to draw," the Dormouse went on, yawning and rubbing its eyes, for it was getting very sleepy, "and they drew all manner of things—everything that begins with an M—"

"Why with an M?" said Alice.

"Why not?" said the March Hare.

Alice was silent.

The Dormouse had closed its eyes by this time, and was going off into a doze. But, on being pinched by the Hatter, it woke up again with a little shriek, and went on, "—that begins with an M, such as mousetraps, and the moon, and memory, and muchness—you know, you say things are 'much of a muchness.' Did you ever see such a thing as a drawing of a muchness!"

"Really, now you ask me," said Alice, very much confused, "I don't think—"

"Then you shouldn't talk," said the Hatter.

This piece of rudeness was more than Alice could bear. She got up in great disgust, and walked off. The Dormouse fell asleep instantly, and neither of the others took the least notice of her going, though she looked back once or twice, half hoping that they would call after her. The last time she saw them, they were trying to put the Dormouse into the teapot.

"At any rate I'll never go *there* again!" said Alice, as she picked her way through the wood. "It's the stupidest tea party I ever was at in all my life!"

427

The Skates of Uncle Richard

CAROL FENNER

Marsha is almost nine years old. Her eyes are brown, and a soft fluff of black hair frames her round, brown face. She dreams of being a figure skater. In her dreams, Marsha is tall and smooth and slender. She is able to spin and fly across the ice. Finally she has a chance to make her dreams come true. Her brother Leonard takes Marsha skating on the frozen lagoon near their house. She is wearing skates that used to belong to her uncle Richard.

Wobbling and swaying, Marsha pushed into her ankles and stayed in one spot. Her arms were sticking out on either side, her ankles bent nearly double. She was practically standing on her ankles.

Leonard grabbed both of her hands. "Now," he ordered, "keep hold of my hands and keep your ankles straight, for cryin' out loud." Then, awkwardly, he began to skate backward, pulling Marsha forward. Her ankles caved in; her ankles bent out. Back and forth, in and out. She wobbled forward on the skates of Uncle Richard. Her head hunched down in front. Her bottom stuck out behind.

It was no fun. Marsha's ankles began to ache, and her bottom was

428

sore from her falling down. Her nose was running. Finally Leonard dragged her to a bench near the little island and left her there. "Be right back," he said and skated away to talk with his friends.

Marsha sat on the bench alone. She wanted to go home, but she didn't know how she would ever get back across the ice to the snowbank where her boots sat. She dropped her head, full of cold and misery.

A scraping sound, ice skates stopping suddenly, made her look up. A man was standing in front of her, smiling. She was so wrapped up in unhappiness that at first she didn't know him. He was very tall, and he had a long, red scarf that trailed over one shoulder. She saw he was leaning toward her, saying something, and she saw his beautiful black cloud of hair, and then she recognized her uncle Richard.

He was saying, "Marsha girl, is that you? Why you lookin' so sad?" Marsha saw he was looking at her skates. "Why don't you lace up your skates properly?" he asked. He bent way over and

touched them thoughtfully. Marsha could see he was puzzled.

"They were your first skates when you were seven," she explained in a low voice. Uncle Richard knelt down in front of her and took one of her feet in both of his hands. "Yeah," he whispered. "They sure were . . . they sure were. . . ." He looked up at her with delight growing in his face. "Those good old skates." He laughed. Then he began to undo the laces, and Marsha thought he was going to take the skates back. But he was saying, "First off, Marsha, you've got to have your skates laced properly. Your feet are falling out of these. They're laced up all wrong."

Uncle Richard straightened the tongue in her boot. He left the bottom lacings loose so that she could wiggle her toes. Then he laced very tightly and evenly across her foot and above her ankle. He tied a knot and laced the rest loosely to the top of the boot. "How does that feel?" he asked after he'd done both feet. It felt great. Like brand-new ankles.

Then Uncle Richard stood her

429

up and began to pull her slowly and evenly across the ice. "Bend your knees, not your middle," he told her. Marsha bent her knees, and her middle straightened right up. She was surprised at how easily she could balance now.

After they had gone a short distance, Uncle Richard said, "You do that real easy, so I want to show you some things to practice here while I get some skating done." First he showed Marsha how to rest her ankles when they got tired. "Stand quiet," he said, "and let your ankles relax right down into your boots . . . right down into the ice. That's important."

Then he said, "Here's something else to practice. Watch close." He pushed forward into one foot and trailed the other behind lightly without touching the ice. "Just bend your knee and lean into it," he said, "nice and easy."

Then he brought the other foot forward and pushed easily into that one. "I push," he said, "and then I glide . . . and then I push with the other foot. And then I glide! Get it?" Marsha nodded. It made good sense.

"Now you practice that for a while. Practice resting your ankles, too, whenever they get tired. Okay?" Marsha nodded and Uncle Richard skated off, his red scarf trailing. She watched to see if he really could skate as well as her mother said.

At first Uncle Richard moved across the ice slowly. Then Marsha saw him reach into his pocket and pull out a tiny radio. He held it next to his ear and began to skate to music no one else could hear. Marsha noticed he glided a long time on one foot before he shifted his weight to the other one. Then he made some smooth, neat turns. His speed quickened. He circled into a spin that blurred his entire outline. The red scarf whipped around him and, as the spin slowed down, the scarf gradually began to unwind.

"Oh," breathed Marsha. "Oh, he is fine. He is really fine." Her uncle began skating backward, leaning his ear into the hand that held the radio. He seemed to be sailing, led around the lagoon by the music.

People began to stop skating to watch Uncle Richard, who now turned and sped forward. Suddenly he swooped and leapt into a single axel, as fine as any Olympic skater's. He circled to a halt and began to skate backward again, disappearing around a bend in the little island.

Alone in the middle of the ice, Marsha felt her ankles begin to wobble with worry. She tried resting them. It worked. They stopped wobbling. "But I can't stand here forever," she thought.

She took a deep breath, bent her knee, and pushed off into her right foot the way Uncle Richard had done. She glided a little, her body balanced over her skating foot. Then she shifted and pushed into her left foot and glided a shaky distance. It worked! Push, glide . . . push, glide. She brought her legs together and glided on both feet all by herself out in the middle of the ice.

She gasped with excitement. It was fun! She pushed off more boldly and glided farther. She did it over again. And again. After a while she rested her ankles.

431

Then she practiced some more . . . push, glide . . . push, glide. She watched her feet. She tried to glide longer on one foot. Push, glide . . . push, glide. She tried to keep her knees bent, her middle straight. Push, glide . . . push, glide.

Suddenly she realized she was at the other end of the lagoon. "My, MY," said a voice behind her. "I thought I left you down at the other end." It was Uncle Richard. He was turning off his radio and smiling. "How'd you get here?" he asked.

"I push-push-glided," said Marsha. "All by myself. No one helped."

"You foolin' me?" asked Uncle Richard, smiling. "Let's see!"

Wobbling only a little at the beginning, Marsha performed her push, glide . . . push, glide. She remembered to keep her skating knee bent. She skated in a medium-sized circle around Uncle Richard and stopped.

"You are one surprising young lady," he said. "You sure learn fast." Marsha was surprised herself. Uncle Richard bent down and looked seriously into her face.

"You ready for another suggestion?" he asked.

Marsha felt, in that moment, that Uncle Richard could see inside her heart better than anyone. The beautiful figure skater of her dreams floated briefly into her mind, but Marsha didn't have time for her now.

"I want to learn how to skate the way you skate," she said. Her voice came out so little and so low that she wondered if he'd heard her. But Uncle Richard touched her cheek softly with his fingertips. He looked very thoughtful for a minute. Then he said quietly, "Okay. We'll work on it."

He stood up. "First off, don't leave your body all bundled down inside your coat. Don't watch your feet. Stretch up. Be proud but not stiff. Watch where you're going. Reach after the sky . . . or the moon . . . or a treetop. Okay? You hear? You remember that?" Marsha nodded, her heart pounding.

"You're a natural," said Uncle Richard. "You can be a super-fine skater, but you'll have to set your mind to it." Marsha nodded again. She understood. Uncle Richard suddenly laughed out loud. "We'll surprise your momma. Maybe we'll shake up the whole world, okay?" he asked.

"Okay," she said, feeling very warm and sure.

"Now you keep practicing," said Uncle Richard. "Next week we'll have another lesson." Marsha beamed at him. "They're a good old pair of skates. Oil the runners, you hear?" Marsha nodded.

Uncle Richard pushed off. She watched him glide away. He turned up the radio again and held it to his ear. It was as if he'd gone through an invisible door onto another winter lagoon that belonged only to him.

Marsha pushed off after him, her head riding high, her round little body stretched taller . . . reaching after him, after the sky or the moon or the tops of the trees. Push, glide . . . push, glide. Past her staring brother she skated. Hardly even a wobble. Proud, not stiff. She glided away on the skates of Uncle Richard, taller and taller and taller, never once falling down.

The Hayloft

Through all the pleasant meadow-side
    The grass grew shoulder-high,
Till the shining scythes went far and wide
    And cut it down to dry.

These green and sweetly smelling crops
    They led in wagons home;
And they piled them here in mountain tops
    For mountaineers to roam.

Here is Mount Clear, Mount Rusty-Nail,
    Mount Eagle, and Mount High;
The mice that in these mountains dwell,
    No happier are than I!

O what a joy to clamber there,
    O what a place for play,
With the sweet, the dim, the dusty air,
    The happy hills of hay!

—Robert Louis Stevenson

434

Glossary

Pronunciation Key

a_, ă_	apple, tan		g	gas, wiggle, sag
ā	acorn, table		ġ	gem, giant, gym
a̍	alone, Donna		gh_	ghost
â	air, care		_gh	though, thought (silent)
ä	father, wand		h_	hat
a̤	all, ball		i_, ĭ_	it, sit
a_e	ape, bake		ī	pilot, pie
ai_	aim, sail		_ï_	babies, machine, *also* onion, savior, familiar
a̍r	calendar		i_e	ice, bite
är	art, park, car		_igh	high, bright
au_	author, Paul		ir	irk, bird, fir
aw	awful, lawn, saw		j_	jam
_ay	say, day		k	kite, ankle, ink
b	bat, able, tub		kn_	knife
c	cat, cot, cut		l	lamp, wallet, tail
ce	cent, ace		_le	table, ample
ch	chest, church		m	man, bump, ham
c̄h	chorus, ache		_mb	lamb, comb
ch	chute		n	no, tent, sun
c̃i	cider, decide		_n̄_	uncle, anger
_ci_	special		_ng	sing, ring
_ck	tack, sick		o_, ŏ_	odd, pot
cy	bicycle		ō	go, no, toe
d	dad		o̍	come, wagon
_dge	edge, judge		ô	off, song
e_, ĕ_	elf, hen		oa_	oat, soap
ē	equal, me		o_e	ode, bone
e̍	moment, loaded		oi_	oil, boil
ea	eat, leap, tea		o͝o	book, nook
_ĕa_	head, bread		o͞o	boot, zoo
ee	eel, feet, see		or	order, normal
er	herd, her		o̍r	motor, doctor
_ew	few, blew		ou_	out, hound
f	far, taffy, off			

ow	owl, town, cow	u̅	truth, true
_ōw	low, throw	u̇	nature
_oy	boy, toy	ṳ	pull, full
p	paper, tap	ur	urge, turn, fur
ph	phone, elephant, graph	ūr	cure, pure
qu_	quick, queen	v	voice, save
r	ram, born, ear	w_	will, wash
s	sun, ask, yes	wh_	white, what
_s	toes, hose	wr_	write
_s̱_	vision, confusion	_x	extra, ax
ss̱	fission	_x_	exist, example
sh	show, bishop, fish	y_	yes, yet
t	tall, sets, bit	_y	baby, happy (when
th	thick, three		it is the only
t͟h	this, feather, bathe		vowel in a final
_tch	itch, patch		unstressed
_t͡i_	nation, station,		syllable)
	also question	_y̆_	cymbal
ṯu	congratulate	_ȳ	cry, sky
u_, ŭ_	up, bus	ẏ	zephyr, martyr
ū	use, cute, *also* granulate	z	zoo, nozzle, buzz

1. If a word ends in a silent *e*, as in **face**, the silent *e* is not marked. If a word ends in *-ed* pronounced **t**, as in **baked**, or **d**, as in **stayed**, no mark is needed. If the ending *-ed* forms a separate syllable pronounced **ėd**, as in **load'ėd**, the *e* has a dot.

2. If there are two or three vowels in the same syllable and only one is marked, as in **beau̅'ty, friĕnd, rōgue,** or **brea̅k,** all the other vowels in the syllable are silent.

3. The Open Court diacritical marks in the Pronunciation Key make it possible to indicate the pronunciation of most unfamiliar words without respelling.

à·ban′dòned *adj.* no longer in use

ab′sènt-mīnd′èd·nèss *n.* forgetfulness

ab·sorb′ *v.* to soak up

ab·surd′ *adj.* ridiculous

Ä·bū̠·e·li′tä a Spanish word that means "little Grandmother"

ac′cess *n.* a way of getting

àc·còm′pà·ny *v.* to sing or play along with

àc·count′ for *v.* to explain

àc·quaint′ *v.* to make known

ac′tū̠·al·ly *adv.* really

Ad′i·ron′dacks *n.* mountains in Northeastern New York

àd·jòurn′ *v.* to dismiss until another time

ad·vanced′ *adj.* ahead of what is expected

ad·vìce′ *n.* a piece of helpful information

ad·vìṣe′ *v.* to inform

aē·ol′i·pile′ *n.* a round container that spins when steam escapes from it

âer′o·dȳ·nam′ics *n.* the science of air motion

Aē′sop *n.* a Greek writer of fables

àf·fect′ *v.* to cause change in

aġe *n.* a period of time in history

ä·hor·ä *adv.* the Spanish word for "now"

aim′lèss·ly *adv.* without purpose

Al′bï·òn

Äl·män′zō

al′ter·nate *v.* to do two things by turns

Ä·mä·pō′lä

am′ble *v.* to walk at an easy pace

ā′mi·à·bly *adv.* in a friendly manner

am′ple *adj.* more than enough

am′pli·fied *adj.* made louder

An·dre·as (Än·drā′às)

àn·noy′ànce *n.* anger

anx·ious·ly (aṅk′shus·ly) *adv.* in a worried way

àp·peal′ *v.* to call on

ap·ple jac·quette (ap′ple jä·ket′) *n.* an apple dumpling (meant to sound French)

Ar′à·bleṣ

ar′id *adj.* dry

ar′ò·mat′ic *adj.* having a pleasant smell

ärt′ful·ly *adv.* cleverly

as·cent′ *v.* to go up

Ā′ṣià *n.* the largest continent

às·sū̠me′ *v.* to take on

às·tron′ò·mer *n.* a person who studies the stars

Ä·thē′nà *n.* the ancient Greek goddess of wisdom, the useful arts, and warfare

àt·tire′ *n.* clothing

au·di′tiòn *v.* to try out for

Aus·tral·ia (Aus·trāl′yà) *n.* a continent Southeast of Asia, between the Indian and Pacific oceans

àu·thor′i·tïes *n.* the people in charge

au′to·mat′i·càl·ly *adv.* working by itself

awk′wàrd *adj.* clumsy

bac·tēr′ï·à *n.* microscopic germs

bän·zaī′ *interj.* a Japanese word that means "hooray"

beâr′ing *n.* a direction

bė·drag′gled *adj.* dirty and limp

Bėl·lĕr′o·phon′ *n.* in Greek mythology, the hero who rode Pegasus and killed the Chimera

Bel·pré, Pu̠·ra (Bel·prā′, Pū̠·rä)

Beth′lé·hèm *n.* a town in northwest Jordan, near Jerusalem

bin *n.* a container for storing something

bōard′èr *n.* a person who rents a room in someone else's house

Bō′az *n.* the second husband of Ruth

bok choy *n.* Chinese cabbage

bound *v.* to run with great leaps

Bre'scĭä *n.* a city in central Lombardy, in northern Italy

Bud•dhist (bụd'ist) *adj.* having to do with Buddhism, an Indian religion

bunt'ing *n.* colorful cloth used for decorations

cạl'drȯn *n.* a large kettle

cap'il•lâr'ĭe̱s *n.* the smallest blood vessels in the body

că•räm'bȧ *interj.* a Spanish word that means "Dear me! or Good gracious!"

cel'ė•brāt'ėd *adj.* well-known

cel'lȧr *n.* an underground room

ce•mï' *n.* a Spanish word that means "a small worshipped object"

cen'taur *n.* a mythical creature, half man (upper body) and half horse

c͡hâr'ȧc•ter *n.* a letter or symbol

c͡härġe *n.* a child left in someone's care

c͡härġed *adj.* full of electricity

chau•dière de clam (c͡hō•dyair' dė clam) "clam chowder," a soup made of clams (meant to sound French)

c͡hĭ•mē'rȧ *n.* a mythical, fire-breathing monster

Chip'pė•wä' *n.* an American Indian tribe in the Lake Superior region

c͡hron'ĭ•cle *n.* a chronological record of events; [often] a newspaper

civ'il *adj.* polite

clam'ȯr•ing *adv.* noisily

clump *v.* to walk heavily

clutch *v.* to hold on to tightly

cō•ag'ū•late *v.* to change from a liquid into a thicker form

col'lȧ•ġen *n.* the protein in some tissue and bone that becomes jellylike when boiled

---

Pronunciation Key

VOWELS: sat, hăve, āble, fäther, ạll, câre, ȧlone; yet, brĕad, mē, loadėd; it, practĭce, pīlot, machïne; hot, nō, ôff, wagȯn; fŏŏt, fōōd; oil, toy; count, town; up, ūse, trụth, pu̱ll; mȳth, baby, crȳ, zephȳr.

CONSONANTS: cent, cider, cycle; c͡horus, c͡hute; gem; light, and though (silent), ghost; iñk, elep͡hant; toe̱s; t͟hem; speci̱al, measu̱re, nati̱on, natu̱re.

---

cȯm•mō'ti̱on *n.* a fuss

com'pėn•sate *v.* to pay back

com'pli•cāt'ėd *adj.* made up of many parts

con'cėn•trāt'ėd *adj.* full of strength

cȯn•clū'si̱ȯn *n.* a final decision

cȯn•di'ti̱ȯn *n.* the state of a thing

con'fi•dėnt•ly *adv.* surely

cȯn•sid'er *v.* to think of

Con•su•e•la (côn•sụ•ā'lä)

cȯn•temp'tu̱•ȯus•ly *adv.* in a way that shows scorn

cȯn•tract' *v.* to shrink

cul'ti•vate *v.* to prepare for planting

cū•rā'tȯr *or* **cū'rȧ•tȯr** *n.* the person in charge of a museum

cū'rĭ•ȯus *adj.* interesting in an odd way

curse *n.* a cause of trouble

cus•tō'dĭ•ȧn *n.* a janitor

Cȳ'ȧ•nē' *n.* in Greek mythology, a river that was the entrance to the underworld

cȳl'in•der *n.* a tube-shaped object

Czech•o•slo•va•ki•a (chec͡h'ȯ•slȯ•vä'kĭ•a) *n.* a country in central Europe

---

damp'ėn *v.* to spoil

dė•bate' *n.* an argument

dė•flāt'ėd *adj.* not filled with air

dė•mand' *n.* a need

De·mē'ter *n.* the ancient Greek goddess of agriculture and the protector of marriage and society.

dė·pos'it·ȯr *n.* a person who puts money into a bank

dė·scend' *v.* to go down

des'per·ȧte·ly *adv.* as a last hope

des'ti·ny *n.* what will happen in the future

dė·ter'mĭned *adj.* to have decided firmly to do something

dė·vice' *n.* something used for a special purpose

dė·vise' *v.* to think up

dė·vour' *v.* to eat up

dif'fer·en'ti̠al *adj.* showing a difference

dim'ly *adj.* not clearly

Din·kel·spiel, Klaus (klous din'kȧl·spiēl)

di·rect'ly *adv.* at once

dis·dain'ful·ly *adv.* in a way that shows one thinks little of

dis·guīse' *n.* clothes that hide who one is

dis·taste' *n.* a feeling of dislike

dis·tress'ful·ly *adv.* unhappily

Djinn (jin) *n.* any of a class of spirits, lower than the angels, capable of appearing in human or animal forms, and influencing mankind for good and evil

dȯ·mes'tic *adj.* tame

dom'i·nate *v.* to stand out

Dor·ē'thȧ

dō'zō a Japanese word that means "if you please"

drĕad'ful·ly *adv.* extremely

du̠'ti·ful·ly *adv.* obediently

dwell *v.* to live in

dwin'dle *v.* to keep growing smaller

ebb *v.* to fall back

ėf·fect' *n.* an ability to change

eld'er *n.* a leader

el'ė·gȧnt *adj.* graceful

el'ė·vā'ti̠on *n.* a feeling of being in a high place

El·i·me·lech (ȧ·li·me'lech)

em·bed'dėd *adj.* stuck firmly

ė·merġe' *v.* to come out of

en·chant'er *n.* a person who casts spells

en·coun'ter *v.* to meet by chance

en·cour'aġ·ing *adj.* causing hope

en·gulf' *v.* to swallow up

ė·nôr'mȯus *adj.* extremely large

en·raġed' *adj.* very angry

en·thū̲'si̠·as'tic *adj.* showing great interest

en·tire'ly *adv.* completely

en·tī'tled *adj.* having the right to

ep'i·der'mis *n.* the outer layer of skin

Ep'i·mē'the·ùs *n.* in classical mythology, a Titan, son of Iapetus and brother of Prometheus and Atlas; the husband of Pandora

Es'tĕr·hä'zў *n.* a Hungarian prince

es'tō es ĭn·cre·ī'ble a Spanish phrase that means "that's unbelievable"

ė·ter'ni·ty *n.* time that goes on forever

ė·vent'ful *adj.* interesting

ėx·aġ'ġer·āt'ėd *adj.* overstated

ex·haust (ėx·aust') *v.* to wear out completely

ėx·pand' *v.* to grow larger

ėx·pos̲e' *v.* to uncover

ėx·tend' *v.* to last

ėx·traôr'din·âr·y *adj.* very unusual

fal′ter *v.* to stumble

fath′om *n.* a measurement of water six feet deep

fa·tigue′ *n.* extreme tiredness

fee′ble *adj.* weak

Fe·li′tä

Ffri′dä

fi′bro·blast′ *n.* a cell that helps form parts of tissue

fic′tion·al *adj.* not real

fixed *adj.* not moveable

fleet′-foot′ed *adj.* able to run fast

flex′i·ble *adj.* easy to bend

fo′cus *n.* a topic

for′ceps *n.* a pair of small pliers

ford *n.* a shallow crossing

for′mer *adj.* from before

Fran·zis·ka (frän·tsis′kä)

frayed *adj.* worn away by rubbing

fric′as·see′ *n.* meat, especially chicken or veal, browned lightly, stewed, and served in a white sauce made with its own stock

fright′ful·ly *adv.* very

frock·coat *n.* a man's old-fashioned dress coat

froth·ing *adj.* foaming

gap′ing *adj.* staring with mouth open

gawk′y *adj.* clumsy

gen·er·a′tion *n.* the time between the birth of parents and the birth of their children

gen′er·os′i·ty *n.* willingness to give

Gi′gi

gir′dle *n.* a belt

glean *v.* to gather

gloom′y *adj.* dark

glum *adj.* sad

Pronunciation Key

VOWELS: sat, hăve, āble, fäther, all, câre, àlone; yet, brĕad, mē, loadèd; it, practĭce, pīlot, machīne; hot, nō, ôff, wagòn; foot, food; oil, toy; count, town; up, ūse, trŭth, pull; mўth, baby, crӯ, zephẏr.

CONSONANTS: cent, cider, cycle; c̄horus, c̱hute; g̀em; light, and though (silent), ghost; iñk, elephant; toe__s__; __th__em; special, mea__s__ure, na__ti__on, na__t__ure.

---

gos′ling *n.* a young goose

grad·u·al·ly (graj′ū·al·ly) *adv.* little by little

grieve *v.* to be very sad

grog′gy *adj.* shaky

gro·tesque (grō·tesk′) *adj.* unusually ugly

Hain′burg *n.* a town in Austria

ham′per *v.* to get in the way of

hast′i·ly *adv.* too quickly

hast′y *adj.* in too much of a hurry

haugh′ti·ly *adv.* proudly

hĕad′y *adj.* exciting

heave *v.* to rise and fall with force

heed′less *adj.* paying no attention

heel *v.* to tilt

hence′forth′ *adv.* from now on

here′a·bouts′ *adj.* around here

hēr′ō·ĭne *n.* a female main character

Her′shèl *n.* an English astronomer (*Also* spelled **Herschel**.)

hes′i·tate *v.* to pause

hoist   to lift up

hos′pi·ta·ble *or* hos·pi′ta·ble *adj.* friendly to guests

hòv′er *v.* to stay in one place in the air

huff *n.* a fit of anger

hum′bly *adv.* politely

441

id′i·o·syn′cra·sy *n.* an odd habit

i′dly *adv.* without purpose

ill′-na′tured·ly *adv.* crossly

il·lu′sion *n.* something imagined

im′age *n.* a likeness

im·pa′tient *adj.* easily annoyed

im·pe′ri·ous·ly *adv.* in a bossy way

im·pressed′ *adj.* strongly moved by

im·pres′sion *n.* a mark

im·pres′sive *adj.* striking and grand

in′cu·ba′tor *n.* a machine for hatching eggs

in·da′ba *n.* a discussion, conference, or consultation between or with South African natives

in·dif′fer·ent·ly *adv.* without caring one way or the other

in·dig′nant·ly *adv.* in an angry way

in ear′nest *adv.* seriously

in′no·cent *adj.* not guilty

in′no·cent·ly *adv.* without trickery

in·oc′u·late *v.* to vaccinate

in·spect′ *v.* to examine

in·spire′ *v.* to cause

in′stinct *n.* an ability one is born with

in·teg′ri·ty *n.* honesty

in·tense′ *adj.* strong

in·tent′ly *adv.* with close attention

in′ter·est *n.* an amount of money paid for the use of a loan

in·ter′pret *v.* to explain the meaning of

in′ter·val *n.* a short period of time

Is′ra·el *n.* a republic in southwest Asia, on the Mediterranean Sea, formed as a Jewish state in May 1948

Jai·me (hī′me)

Ji′ya

Jo·hann (yō′hänn)

Jo·sé (hō·ze′)

Ju′dah

ki·mo′no *n.* a loose, wide-sleeved robe, fastened at the waist with a wide sash

kins′man *n.* a male relative

Ki′tä·mu′ra

Krä′ka·to′a *n.* an island volcano in Indonesia

laced *adj.* streaked

la′dle *v.* to spoon out

large′ly *adv.* mostly

Läs Mä·ri′as *n.* a village in Puerto Rico

La·val′ *n.* a city in France

lay waste *v.* to destroy

lean-to (lean-tu) *n.* a shed attached to the side of a building

Le·o·nar·do da Vin·ci (Lē·ò·när′dō dà Vin′chi) *n.* an Italian painter, sculptor, architect, musician, engineer, mathematician, and scientist, 1452–1519

Ley′den jär *n.* a glass jar lined inside and outside with tin foil which stores a form of electricity

lim′ber *adj.* able to bend easily

loll *v.* to hang down loosely

lope *v.* to move in an easy, bounding manner

lure *v.* to tempt

lux′u·ry *n.* an unneeded thing

Ly·ci·a (lish′i·à) *n.* an ancient country in southwestern Asia Minor, later a Roman province

Mad′·a·gas′·car *n.* an island (French) in the Indian Ocean

Ma·dell′

ma′·jor·do′·mo a man in charge of a group of servants

Mal·do·na′·do, Fe·li′·ci·dad

Ma·mi

mar *v.* to spoil

Mar·i·cao (mär·i·cow′) *n.* a village in Puerto Rico

Ma·thi′·as

mat·zah (mät′sà) **ball** *n.* a kind of ball-like dumpling, usually served in a clear soup

mech′·a·ni·za′·tion *n.* the use of machines to do the work of people

me gus·ta (me gūs′tä) a Spanish phrase that means "I like it"

mem′·brane *n.* a thin layer of skin

Mid′·e·wi·win *n.* an old American Indian religion

mi′·grate *v.* to move from one place to another as the seasons change

mim′·e·o·graph′ *v.* to make copies on a special machine

min′·i·a·ture *adj.* very tiny

mi′·nor *adj.* not serious

Mi·yo

Mo′·ab *n.* an ancient kingdom east of the Dead Sea, in what is now Jordan

Mohr, Nich·o·las·a (mōr, nich′ō·läs′à)

Moi′·she

Mon′·ti·cel′·lo *n.* the estate of Thomas Jefferson, near Charlottesville, Virginia

mood′·y *adj.* having changeable feelings

mor′·tal *n.* a human being

Mount O·lym′·pus *n.* 1. a mountain in northeastern Greece 2. mythical home of major Grecian gods

mū·chä′·chōs *n.* a Spanish word that means "boys"

murk′·y *adj.* dark

mus′·ty *adj.* having a stale or moldy smell

Nā·ō′·mi *n.* the mother-in-law of Ruth

nün′·cä tän fe·liz′ a Spanish phrase that means "never so happy"

nўmph *n.* a forest or water spirit

Ō′·bed *n.* in the Bible, the son of Ruth and Boaz

òb·serve′ *v.* to notice

òb·tain′ *v.* to get

ob′·vi·ous·ly *adj.* clearly

òc·cā′·siòn·àl *adj.* happening now and then

oc′·cū·pànt *n.* one who lives in or uses a space

o·cean·ar·i·um (ō′·s̲hēa·när′·ï·um) *n.* a building in which live sea animals or plants are kept

òf·fend′·èd *adj.* insulted

on stand bȳ *adj.* ready

o·pin′·iòn *n.* what one thinks about something

ò·rig′·i·nate *v.* to begin

Ôr′·pah *n.* a woman who lived in the Biblical country Moab

Ō′·saġe *n.* a member of the American Indian tribe that speaks the Osage language dialect

443

out•dis′tánce *v.* to outrun

ō•ver•cȯme′ *adj.* made helpless

ō′ver•sē•er *n.* a manager

pà•lav′er *n.* a meeting or conversation

pall *n.* a dark covering (special meaning in this story)

Pä•pī

Pa•qui•to (pä•kī′tō)

Pa•pin, Di•o•ny•si•us (pa•pa′, dī′ȯ•nȳ′shī•us) a French scientist

pär′ti•cle *n.* a small bit

pär•tic′ū•lȧr•ly *adv.* especially

pā′trĭ•ot′ic *adj.* showing love for one's country

Peg′à•sus *n.* in Greek mythology, a winged horse

Per•rine′

Pėr•seph′ȯ•nē *n.* in Greek mythology, a daughter of Zeus and Demeter

per•suade (per•swade′) *v.* to convince another to agree

pet′ty *adj.* unimportant

Phâr′aōh *n.* a title of an ancient Egyptian king

Pi′mà *n.* a member of an American Indian tribe in southern Arizona and northern Mexico

pit′y•ing•ly *adv.* showing that one feels sorry for someone

plate•lets (plāte′lĭts) *n.* small, platelike bodies, especially a blood platelet

plat′y•pus *n.* duckbilled animal

plum′mėt *v.* to drop straight down

poisẹd *adj.* ready to act

pon′der *v.* to think about

Por′por•ä, Nic′co•lo an Italian composer and teacher of singing

pȯs•sẹss′ *v.* to have

prac′ti•càl *adj.* sensible

pre′ci̇ous *adj.* very dear

pred′á•tȯr *n.* an animal that hunts other animals for food

prẹs′ėnt•ly *adv.* soon

prė•sėrve′ *v.* to keep alive

prī′mȧr•y *adj.* main

prin′ci•ple *n.* a law of nature

prȯ•ceed′ *v.* to go ahead

proc′ess *n.* a way of doing something

prof′it *n.* an amount of money that is left over after expenses have been paid

Prȯ•mē′thē•us *n.* in Greek mythology, a giant god who stole fire from Mount Olympus and gave it to human beings

prompt′ly *adv.* right away

prȯ•pōṣ′àl *n.* a suggestion

prȯ•test′ *v.* to object

prō′tȯ•plaṣm *n.* the jellylike material, necessary for life

puḷ′lėt *n.* a young hen

pun•chà′yet *n.* a Hindi word for "long discussion" or "meeting"

raġe *v.* to burn with great force

rañk *v.* to classify

rasp′ing *adj.* making a harsh, scraping noise

rē•às•sured′ *adj.* feeling sure again

rē′cėnt *adj.* fairly new

rė•cite′ *v.* to repeat from memory

rec′ȯl•lec′ti̇on *n.* a memory

rec′ȯm•mend *v.* to suggest something as worthwhile

rė•gret′ *v.* to feel sorry about

rē′in•fōrce′ *v.* to strengthen

rė•lease′ *v.* to let go

rė•lïef′ *n.* a feeling that things are improved

re•lieved' *adj.* freed of worry

re•luc'tant•ly *adv.* unwillingly

rem•i•nisce (rem'i•nis) *v.* to talk of past experiences

rep're•sent' *v.* to stand for

rep'u•ta'tion *n.* what people think of a person or a thing

re'qui•em *n.* music written for a funeral or to honor the dead

re•sent' *v.* to feel angry and insulted

re•sist' *v.* to keep from giving in to

re•tire' *v.* to disappear

re•un'ion *n.* a gathering of people who have been separated

re•veal' *v.* to show

re•volve' *v.* to go around

Ri•car'do

rift *n.* a break in friendship

rig'id *adj.* unbending

roc *n.* a fabulous bird of great size and strength

Roh•rau (rō'rau) *n.* a village in southern Austria

roy'al•ty *n.* kings and queens and their relatives

Rud'yard

rue'ful•ly *adv.* showing that one feels sorry about something

rum'mage *v.* to search through

runt *n.* an unusually small animal

sac'ri•fice *v.* to give up [something]

sam'u•ri' *n.* a member of the warrior class in Japan in earlier times

San Juan de la Mon•ta•na (sän hwän de lä môn•tä'nä)

Sän'ti•ä'gō

scal'a•wag' *n.* a mischief maker

scârce'ly *adv.* hardly

scorch'ing *adj.* very hot

scorn *n.* a feeling that someone is not good enough

scoun'drel *n.* a rascal

scowl *v.* to frown

scrōll *n.* a roll of paper to be written or painted on

'scru'ci•āt•ing *adv.* made-up word for ex•cru'ci•āt•ing•ly, meaning "in an extreme or "extremely" manner"

scur'ry *v.* to scamper

se•cūre' *adj.* having enough money

seem'ing•ly *adv.* in a way that appears to be

seep *v.* to leak slowly

self'-con'fi•dence *n.* the belief in one's own ability to do well

self'-re•lī'ant *adj.* able to depend on oneself

self'-re•spect' *n.* regard for one's own character and reputation

Se•ñor (sen•yôr') *n.* a word that means "mister" in Spanish

Se•ñor (sen•yôr') Säl'vä•dôr

sen•sā'tion *n.* a feeling

sen'si•tĭve *adj.* able to feel

se•vĕr'i•ty *n.* harshness

sheaf *n.* a bundle of grain

Sic•i•ly (Sis'i•ly) *n.* the largest island in the Mediterranean Sea, owned by Italy

sight′-read *v.* to sing or play music at first sight

sim′i·lar·ly *adv.* in the same way

sin′ew·y *adj.* muscular

sin′is·ter *adj.* seeming dangerous

slough (sluf) *v.* to fall off

smoth′er·y *adj.* without fresh air

smoul′der·ing *adj.* smoking

sol·emn·ly (sol′ĕm·ly) *adv.* seriously

sol′i·tar′y *adj.* alone

so′när *n.* a way of finding objects underwater by bouncing sound waves off them

splen′did *adj.* wonderful

state′ly *adj.* grand

stĕad′y *v.* to hold still

steed *n.* a high-spirited horse

stew′ard *n.* a servant in charge

stout *adj.* strongly built

strewn *adj.* scattered

stride *v.* to walk with long steps

suave (swäve) *adj.* smooth

sub·side′ *v.* to die down

sub′stance *n.* a special material

Su̱′gi

su̱it′a·ble *adj.* proper

suit′or *n.* a man who is trying to win a woman's love

sulk′i·ly *adv.* in a bad-tempered way

sum′mon *v.* to call up

sup′ple *adj.* able to bend easily

sur·round′ing *adj.* nearby

sur·vive′ *v.* to stay alive

swag′ger *v.* to walk boldly

swel′ter·ing *adj.* very hot and humid

sym′me·try *n.* balance

sym′pa·thet′ic *adj.* understanding

sy·ringe′ *n.* a tool for squirting, pumping, or spraying liquids.

tam′a·risk *n.* an ornamental Mediterranean shrub or small tree having slender, feathery branches

Tas·mā′ni·a *n.* an island south of Australia

tem′per·a·men′tal *adj.* easily upset

tex′tile *adj.* cloth-making

three′-prônged′ *adj.* having three pointed ends

Tī′tō *n.* president of Yugoslavia 1953–1980

trace *n.* a sign of someone

tra·di′tion·al *adj.* handed down from generation to generation

trans·fer′ *v.* to move from one place to another

trans·pâr′ent *adj.* easy to see through

trea′cle *n.* molasses

trib′ute *n.* an honor

trī′fle *v.* to tease

Trī′nä

trī·umph′ant·ly *adv.* in a way that shows joy at winning

trod′den *adj.* walked upon

trudge *v.* to walk heavily

um·bil′i·cal cord′ *n.* a cord through which an unhatched chick or unborn baby receives food

un·beâr′a·ble *adj.* impossible to put up with

un′der·world′ *n.* the home of the dead

un·found′ed *adj.* not based on fact

un·grate′ful *adj.* not thankful

un·just′ly *adv.* unfairly

un·nat′u·ral *adj.* unusual

urge *v.* to force onward

ur′ġent•ly *adv.* in a way that cannot be
 ignored

ut′ter•ly *adv.* completely

Val•dez, Flavio (flä′vi•ō, väl•des′)

vär′i•ous *adj.* several different

veer *v.* to change direction

ven *v.* a Spanish word that means "come"

vent *n.* an opening

ven′tu̇re *v.* to dare

vė•ran′dȧ *n.* porch

ver′bȧl *adj.* spoken

vī′brate *v.* to move back and forth rapidly

Vi•en′na *n.* a part in, and the capital of,
 Austria

vi′si̇ȯn *n.* imagination

vol′un•teer′ *n.* one who offers to help

wêa′ri•ly *adv.* tiredly

Win′nė•bā′gō *n.* an American Indian tribe
 now living in Green Bay, Wisconsin, and
 northeastern Nebraska

Zeūs *n.* in Greek mythology, the god of the
 heavens chief of the gods

Pronunciation Key

VOWELS: sat, hăve, āble, fäther, a̤ll, câre, ȧlone; yet,
brĕad, mē, lȯadėd; it, practĭce, pīlot, machïne; hot,
nō, ôff, wagȯn; fo͝ot, fo͞od; oil, toy; count, town;
up, ūse, trṳth, pṳll; mȳth, baby, crȳ, zephȳr.

CONSONANTS: cent, cider, cycle; c̄horus, c̲hute; ġem;
light, and though (silent), ġhost; iñk, elep̄hant; toe̲s;
t̲hem; spec̲ial, meaṣure, nat̲ion, natu̲re.